MARCHING
ALONG

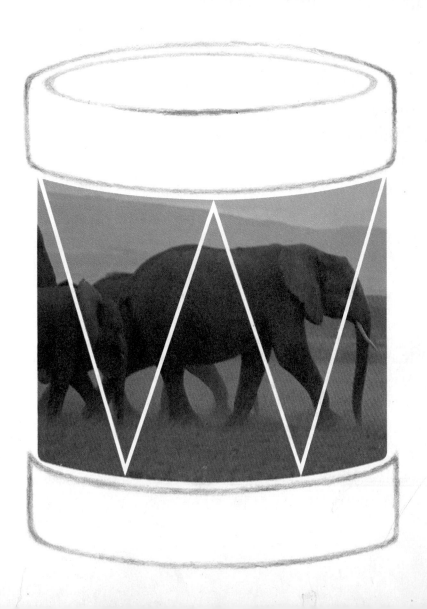

CONSULTANTS

Mildred Bailey	**Teresa Flores**	**Nancy Mayeda**
Rose Barragan	**Charles Hacker**	**Kenneth Smith**
Barbara Burke	**P.J. Hutchins**	**Lydia Stack**
Barbara B. Cramer	**George Jurata**	**Mary Wigner**
Wilma J. Farmer		

Executive Editor: *Sandra Maccarone*
Senior Editor: *Ronne Kaufman*
Associate Editor: *Eleanor Franklin*
Design Director: *Leslie Bauman*
Assistant Design Director: *Kay Wanous*
Production Director: *Barbara Arkin*
Production Manager: *Trudy Pisciotti*

D.C. HEATH AND COMPANY

Lexington, Massachusetts/Toronto, Ontario

Cover, Front Matter, Unit Openers designed by *Thomas Vroman Associates, Inc.* Illustrators: John Freas, pp. 14-17; Diane DeGroat, pp. 18-22; Leigh Grant, pp. 24-28; John Wallner, pp. 30-37; Ron LeHew, pp. 39-47; Lawrence diFiori, pp. 49-54; Angela Adams. pp. 58-64; Jeffrey Terreson. pp. 66-67; Pamela Carroll, pp. 68-73; Melanie Arwin, pp. 84-92; Renee Daily, pp. 96-103; Angela Adams, pp. 105-109; Marilyn Bass, pp. 111-116; Don Almquist, pp. 118-119; Allen Davis, pp. 120-128; Jan Palmer, pp. 132-140; Marian Ebert, p. 142; Marian Ebert, p. 143; John Wallner, pp. 144-151; Marilyn Bass, pp. 154-159; John Freas, pp. 161-168; Ron LeHew, pp. 172-178; John Wallner, pp. 180-184; Diane de Groat, pp. 186-188; John Wallner, pp. 189-196; Jan Palmer, pp. 198-206; Loring Eutemy, pp. 210-219; N. Jo Smith, pp. 221-226; Diane de Groat, p. 227; John Wallner, p. 228; Len Ebert, pp. 229-231; Yvette Banek, pp. 232-238.

Photo Credits: R. S. Virdee, Shostal, cover and p. 1; Elliott Erwitt, Magnum, pp. 8-9; William Hamilton, Shostal, p. 10; James Foote. Photo Researchers, p. 11; Russell Abraham, Jeroboam, p. 12; Katrina Thomas, Photo Researchers, pp. 56-57; B. Anderson, Shostal, pp. 94-95; Robert A. Isaacs, Photo Researchers, pp. 130-131; Courtesy of Macy's, pp. 170-171; William Hubbell, Woodfin Camp, pp. 208-209.

ACKNOWLEDGMENTS

Every reasonable effort has been made to trace the owners of copyright materials in this book, but in some instances this has proven impossible. The publishers will be glad to receive information leading to more complete acknowledgments in subsequent printings of the book, and in the meantime extend their apologies for any omissions.

To the estate of Frances Duggar for "A Snail Takes a Walk" by Frances Duggar; reprinted by permission of the author's estate.

To Scholastic Magazines, Inc., for "Winter Garden" by Rebecca Kalusky; reprinted by permission from *News Trails,* © 1964 by Scholastic Magazines, Inc.

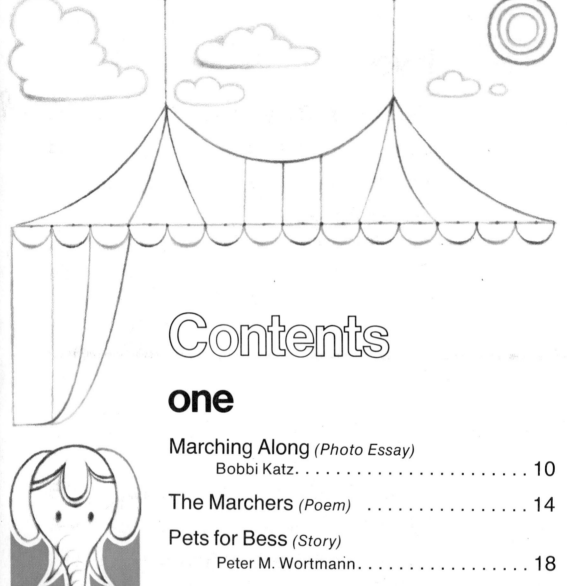

Contents

one

two

three

four

five

six

one

Marching Along

The beat of a drum

The boom of a band

The tap of a foot

The clap of a hand

The smile of a clown

The sound of a song

Mean that the parade

Is marching along!

Bobbi Katz

14

The Marchers

Down the street the marchers came,
    With colors flying bright.
In rows of ten they marched along,
    All looking to the right.

Then came three girls who marched and whirled
    In sunny yellow skirts.
Next came the band, in tall white hats,
    And white-and-yellow shirts.

Then floats of girls with flowers bright
    Came riding down the street.
As each went by, the crowd would shout
    In time to marching feet.

You should have seen those marchers proud,
    Those pretty girls and floats.
They looked as if they were riding
    In white-and-yellow boats!

Then came the rain, and all those floats,
   With pretty, smiling girls,
Began to melt and float away
   In white-and-yellow whirls.

The marchers could not march in rain,
   And so they all went home.
The band went, too. So did the crowd.
   And there I stood, alone.

PETS FOR BESS

"I would have lots of pets if I were rich," said Bess. "All my pets would be very big. And they all would live here in my room."

"I don't know," said Pat with a laugh. "That sounds like a lot of pets for such a little room."

"I guess you are right," said Bess. "Just one nice pet would be fine with me."

"Let's take a walk on the beach," said Pat. "Maybe we can find some shells."

"Shells don't make very good pets," said Bess.

"I know, but it's such a nice day outside," said Pat. "And who knows what we might find at the beach!"

Pat could not see, so Bess took his
hand as they walked. "There are some
shells here in the sand," she said.
"They are all wet and they gleam."

Bess handed Pat some of the shells.
He started to clean the sand off.

"I can't see them gleam, but I can
feel how smooth they are," Pat said.
"We make a very good team. You can
find all the shells, and I can clean them."

Bess placed some shells in Pat's hand.
Pat started to clean them off, too.
"Wait!" he said. "What are these?"

"They look much like snail shells,"
said Bess.

"No," said Pat. "I can feel that these
are not just shells. I think these two
snails are still living."

21

Bess started to laugh. "Finding a pet wasn't hard at all," she said. "We didn't need to be rich. All we needed was to work like a team."

"And a good team is just what we are!" said Pat.

Bess and Pat took the snails home. They found a glass case, and they cleaned it.

"I was thinking about some very big pets," smiled Bess. "But they were much too big for this case."

"Snails are funny pets," said Pat. "But they are just the right pets for you!"

THINK ABOUT IT

1. At first, what kind of pets did Bess want?
2. Why did Pat and Bess make a good team?
3. How could Pat know that snails were living in the shells?
4. Do you think snails are funny pets? Why or why not?
5. What kind of pet would you want? Why?

Why Are Some Days Cloudy?

In one place, a boy goes outside and looks up at the dark sky. He says, "It looks snowy today."

Not too far away, a girl looks up at the sun. She says, "It is going to be a fair day today. There are no clouds in the sky."

And in a place not too far from the girl, a man goes outside his house. He feels drops of water on his face and hair. He says, "I will need a hat today to keep my hair dry."

How can the same day be snowy, fair, and rainy in three places? Why does a sunny day sometimes become cloudy? Why does a cloudy day sometimes become snowy or rainy?

Air is a gas that can't be seen. It is all around us. As it moves, it takes in drops of water. When the air has little water in it, the sky is fair and we can feel the sun. When the air takes in too much water, rain or snow will begin to fall.

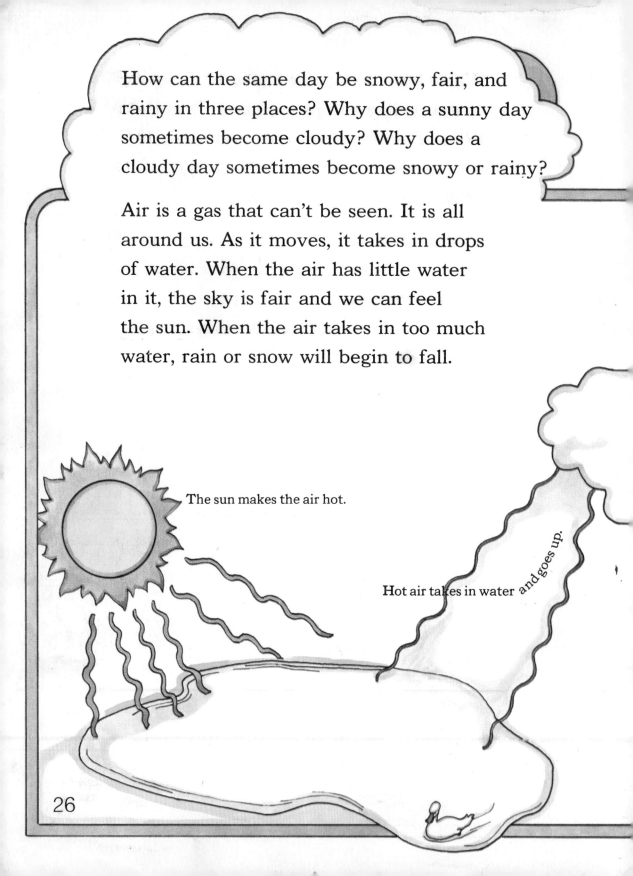

The sun makes the air hot.

Hot air takes in water and goes up.

When hot air begins to take in a lot
of water, it goes up into the sky.
When the drops of water in the hot air
become cool, they turn into clouds.
Then the day will be cloudy.

If the air in the sky is cold, the clouds
will be filled with little drops of ice.
Some clouds don't hold these drops
of ice for long. Soon the drops of ice
will start to fall.

The water cools.
It turns into clouds.

Drops of ice fall from the clouds.

On hot days,
the ice melts.

On cold days,
the ice doesn't
melt.

As the drops of ice fall, they may hit hot air below. If they do, they will melt and turn to rain.

If the drops of ice fall into cold air below, they will not melt. Then snow will fall.

Go outside on the next cloudy day. If it is a cold day, do you think snow or rain will fall? If it is a hot day, do you think snow or rain will fall?

28

1. What does the air take in as it moves?

2. On a sunny day, how much water is in the air? Is there a lot, or is there just a little?

3. What makes a day cloudy?

4. If a day is cold and cloudy, what might fall?

5. If a day is hot and cloudy, what might fall?

6. What kinds of days do you like best? Why?

The Singing Hen

Part One

Long ago on a small farm,
there lived a boy and his mother.
They didn't have any cows or pigs
or any ducks or sheep. All they had
was a hen called Penny.

Penny wasn't much of a hen, but she was
good at one thing. She could get the boy
and his mother out of bed. When the sun
came up, Penny flew to the top of the house.
First, she would spin around. Then she
would sing a little song. That's right.
Penny was a singing hen!

One day, the boy's mother said, "We need
a cow, not a singing hen. If we had
a cow, we could sell the milk."

"I will get a cow," said the boy. "I
will take Penny into town and trade her."

"That's a good thought," said his mother.
"But I don't think you will get a cow
for a singing hen."

The boy threw the hen under his arm and
started off.

Not far from town, the boy saw a cutter
of wood. "Oh," said the cutter. "It is
you." He started to laugh. "Are you
still a spinner of yarns?"

The boy smiled. "Let's not talk about me.
Where are YOU going?"

"To town," said the cutter of wood. "I
have brought my cow along to trade it."

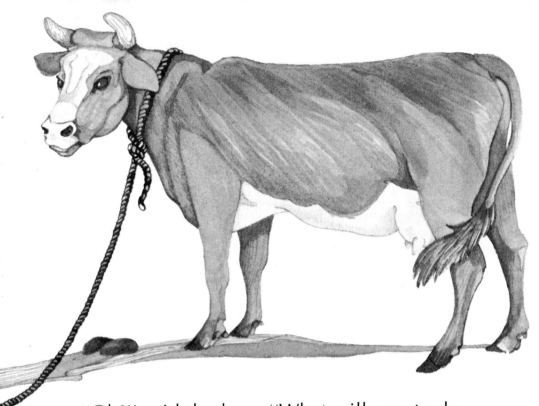

"Oh?" said the boy. "What will you trade
it for?"

"For something that will tell me the time,"
said the cutter. "Each day, I sleep
very late. That is not a good thing
for a cutter of wood to do."

"Why is that?" asked the boy.

"Well," said the cutter. "There are
lots of cutters who sell their wood
in town. If I don't get there first,
I won't sell very much wood."

Part Two

"You ought to trade your cow
for my hen," said the boy. "Penny
is just what you need."

The cutter smiled. "That is a fine hen,"
he said. "But I need something to get
me up with the sun. Hens can't do that."

"This hen can," said the boy. "It sings
when the sun comes up."

"You sound like a bragger," said
the cutter. "No one but a bragger
would say that his hen could sing."

"I am not bragging," said the boy.
"My mother and I need a cow. If Penny
doesn't get you up with the sun, I
will give you back your cow."

The cutter made a face and blew out
some air. He thought and thought. Then
he blew out some more air.

"All right," said the cutter. "You may
be spinning a yarn about that hen. You
may be a bragger. But I will soon find out.
Here is my cow. Give me the hen
you brought."

The boy threw the hen to the cutter.
"Penny will sing for you when the sun
comes up. You will get to town first.
You will sell more wood."

"You may be right," said the cutter. "I
ought to sell more wood."

The boy took the cow and went home. When
his mother saw the cow, she smiled. "Where
did you get that fine cow?" she asked.

"From the cutter," said the boy. "He
needed a singing hen to get him up. We
needed a cow."

The next day, the singing hen got
the cutter up with the sun. But the boy
and his mother stayed in bed very late.

"Oh, my!" said the boy. "I guess we
will have to teach this cow to sing."

THINK ABOUT IT

1. Who was named Penny?
2. What was Penny good at doing?
3. Why did the boy trade Penny?
4. Why did the boy and his mother stay
   in bed very late?
5. Do you think the boy made a good trade?
   Why?

TIMMY TURTLE

Part One

Timmy Turtle was very sad. He wanted
to play with the other turtles. But they
were all up on the bank.

"I would give anything in the world to be
up on that bank," said Timmy.

The other turtles went up the bank
all the time, but Timmy just didn't try.

39

"I would if I could," he said. "But I can't."

"Why don't you come up on the bank and
roll that rock with us?" asked one
of the turtles.

"There's nothing I would like better,"
said Timmy. "But I can't get up the bank."

"How do you know if you don't try?"
asked the other turtle.

"I know that I can't. I would if I could,
but I can't," said Timmy.

Just then, an old turtle called Grandpa
went by. When he heard the other turtle,
Grandpa sided with Timmy.

"Timmy must take his time," said Grandpa.
"Someday he will try. Then he will know
what he can do and what he can't do."

When he heard Grandpa side with Timmy,
the other turtle said nothing. He
just went up the bank to play
with the other turtles.

Timmy sat under the bank with Grandpa.
They could not see the other turtles
playing. They could hear them laughing.

"I hate sitting here and listening
to the others," said Timmy. "I would give
anything in the world to go up there!"

Part Two

Grandpa said, "I will go up and see why
they are laughing. Won't you come, Timmy?"

"I would if I could," said Timmy. "But I can't."

Grandpa heard Timmy, but he said nothing.
He smiled and started up the bank.

A big rock began to roll down the bank.
"Look out!" Timmy shouted. It was no use.
The rock hit Grandpa and rolled on.

Over and over rolled Grandpa. He landed
on his back in the sand. "Timmy, Timmy,"
he called. "Come and help me!"

"I hear you, Grandpa! I'm coming as fast
as I can," said Timmy. "Are you OK?"

"I landed on my back," said Grandpa.
"Listen, my son. YOU must roll me over."

"I would if I could," said Timmy. "But
you are too big for me to roll over."

"You must try, my son," said Grandpa.
"It's not good for an old turtle like me
to be on his back in the sun."

Timmy shaded his face and looked up.
"I don't think there's anything I can do,"
he said. "But I will try."

"Good!" said Grandpa. "Hold on to my shell.
I will rock a little to get you started."

Timmy held on to Grandpa's shell. They
started to rock. They rocked and rocked,
but Grandpa didn't turn over.

"I hate to say it, my son," said Grandpa.
"But maybe you are right. Maybe I am
too big for you to roll over by yourself."

"I can't give up now," said Timmy. "Let's
try rocking fast."

Timmy held on to Grandpa one more time.
Then they rocked and rocked and rocked.
Soon Grandpa was rocking so fast that
Timmy could not hold on.

ROCK, ROCK, ROCK! Up went Grandpa,
way up on one side. ROCK, ROCK, ROCK!
Over he went, and down he came, landing
right side up!

"We did it! We did it!" shouted Timmy.

"Yes!" said Grandpa. "I'm proud of you, my son! You did it! Come on, let's go up the bank."

Timmy wanted to go up the bank. But for a time, he shaded his face. Then he looked at Grandpa's back going up the bank. "I would if I could, but . . . I can try!" he said. And up the bank he went!

"Good turtle!" said Grandpa. "Now, let's find the others."

Grandpa started right off, and Timmy went with him. Soon they saw the other turtles. Timmy smiled and said, "Now I know what I can do, Grandpa. All I had to do was TRY!"

THINK ABOUT IT

1. What did Timmy Turtle want to do?
2. What did the rock do when it rolled down the bank?
3. How did Timmy help Grandpa?
4. How did Timmy feel when he helped Grandpa?
5. What did Timmy find out about *trying*?
6. Name three things you can't do. How hard did you try to do them?

NO SMILES TODAY

Jimmy's sister seemed to smile all the time. She was just a happy baby. She did cry now and then, but soon she stopped and smiled. One day, Jimmy came home from school and ran into the house.

"Hi, Dad. How is my little sister with the big smile?" he asked. "You both look a little sad today."

49

"I'm glad you're home," said Dad.
"Your baby sister is not smiling
today. She's crying and crying. I know
what's the matter. Her mouth hurts.
Her teeth are starting to come in.
They're giving her a lot of pain."

"I see she's putting her hand in her
mouth," said Jimmy. "Did you try
holding her and singing to her?"

"That didn't help much," said Dad.

"Did you try to push her in the buggy?" Jimmy asked.

"A buggy ride didn't help her," said Dad. "Those teeth hurt a lot."

"How about putting her in her play pen with her toys?" said Jimmy.

"See for yourself. She just holds on to the bar and wants to get out," said Dad. "But, you can see she's getting steady on her feet. Soon she will let go of the bar and stand alone."

"I know how she's feeling," said Jimmy.
"When I fell and hit my head, it hurt
for a long time. Nothing made me feel
like smiling when my head hurt."

"Maybe you can help, Jimmy," said Dad.
"I haven't read all these papers yet.
They're very long, and I should mark
them for my class tonight We're going
to eat as soon as Mom gets home from
work. We're having fish, and I haven't
started to cook yet."

"You're asking the right one," said
Jimmy. "You're good at cooking and
marking papers. One thing I'm good at
is getting my baby sister to smile. We
both have work to do. First I will try
my funny faces."

It seemed to be working. The baby
looked up and stopped crying.

"I know," said Jimmy. "Today in school
we read about how to make paper hats.
How would you like me to make one for you?"

Jimmy put some paper on a stool.
With steady hands, he made the paper
into a hat. The baby was looking at
what he was doing. She didn't think
about her teeth. He put the hat on his
head. She smiled a little. He put the
hat on her head. She smiled a lot. Then
she started to laugh.

The baby felt better. That made Jimmy
feel proud.

1. Was Jimmy's sister a happy baby?

2. How did Jimmy's sister feel when her teeth started to come in?

3. What did Jimmy do to make his sister feel better?

4. What kind of boy do you think Jimmy is?

5. What can you do to make someone happy?

6. How does it feel to make someone happy?

THE BOY FROM ZORGO

Pat Lee looked at the small boy who
was standing next to her.

"Must Butch come to the store with us?"
she asked her mother.

"You both need jackets," said Mrs. Lee.

"Well, why does he have to keep
that THING on his head?" asked Pat.
"He must think he is from the moon."

"Don't be that way, Pat," said Mrs. Lee.
Then the bus came, and they all got on.

"We will look for Pat's jacket first,"
said Mrs. Lee, putting away her wallet.
"Then we will look at a jacket for Butch."

"Must I look for HER jacket?" said Butch.
"I want to look at the toys."

"OK," said Mrs. Lee. "When we need you,
Pat and I will come and get you."

When they got to the store, Butch went
right to the space toys. "My spaceship
has more rockets on it," someone said.

Butch turned to the boy who was standing next to him. The boy's hair was bright green. His mouth was yellow. The mouth ran up and down the boy's purple face!

"I like spaceships more than I like cars or trucks. Don't you?" asked the boy with the green hair, yellow mouth, and purple face.

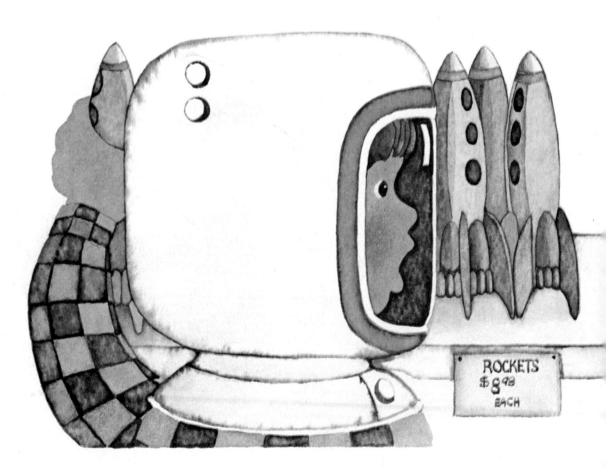

ROCKETS
$8.98
EACH

Before Butch could say a word, the boy
went on. "We use them all the time on Zorgo."

"ON ZORGO!" shouted Butch. "Don't you
live here on Earth?"

"No," said the boy. "I just came down
to Earth for the day. My spaceship is
on top of the store. What's your name?"

"My name is Butch," said Butch.

The boy laughed. "And mine is Zerp.
You look just like a moon boy!"

Before Butch could say anything, a lady
came along. She was with the man who
sold the toys.

"Would you boys mind moving over
to the trucks and cars?" asked the man.
"We want to look at the space toys."

Butch pulled Zerp back a little.

"Your little girl would like this spaceship,"
the man told the lady.

"She would not!" shouted Zerp. "That ship won't fly with just three rockets!"

"How do YOU know?" asked the man.

"I fly a ship all the time," said Zerp. "That's how I know."

The lady and the man both shook their heads.

"He does so!" shouted Butch. "Zerp is not from Earth! He comes from Zorgo."

"Maybe so," said the lady. "But this looks just like the other rocket I bought for her. She wants two of them."

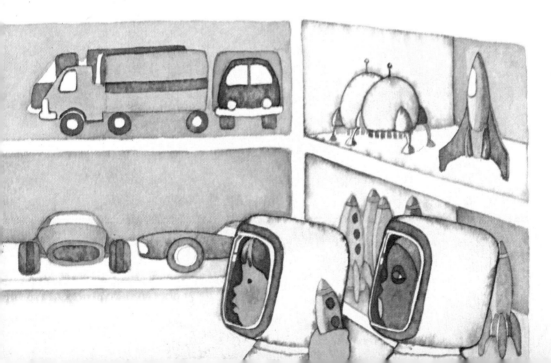

"Well, that's not the right kind," said
Zerp. "I should know!"

The lady laughed. Then she took out
her wallet and bought the rocket.

Zerp began to pull Butch by the arm. "It
is getting late," he said. "Let's go."

"I can't," said Butch. "I have to shop
for a jacket with my mother and sister."

"Get a thick one," said Zerp.
"It's cold on Zorgo. Come
see me sometime!"

1. How does Pat feel about what Butch has on his head?

2. What color is Zerp's hair?

3. Why does Butch need a thick jacket?

4. If you wanted to look as if you came from space, how would you dress? Make a drawing of how you would look.

Caught in a Storm

At first, the air was very still.
    The moon above was bright.
We walked along and listened to
    The small sounds of the night.

Then in a wink the moon went in.
    The road ahead was black.
"I felt a drop!" said Kay. "I think
    It's time that we went back."

We turned to go, but as we did,
    I tripped and almost fell.
Kay caught my arm to hold me up,
    But I began to yell.

For as I watched, the tall trees shook.
  The night was filled with sound.
The crashing, flashing sky was bright.
  The rain began to pound.

Then Kay yelled, too, and off we ran
  As fast as we could go.
You would have done the same if you
  Had seen that big storm blow!

67

Beavers

Have you seen beavers in the woods?
Do you know what they look like?

PARTS OF A BEAVER

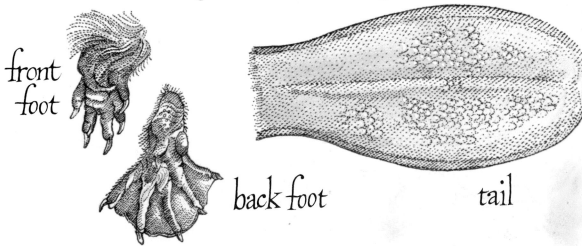

front foot

back foot

tail

Beavers have thick, brown fur coats and big flat tails. They use their strong tails to help them swim. Their front teeth are so big and strong that they can use them to cut down small trees.

Beavers have small front feet that they use to dig. Their big back feet are webbed, just like a duck's. These webbed feet help them swim.

Beavers learn to do many things. They can swim under water. They can build things. They can also find most of the things they need to build something. Beavers work best in water.

69

Beavers like to build their houses
in the water. They like to live
where the water is not too shallow.
When the water is too shallow, beavers
build a dam out of small trees and twigs.
The dam goes from one bank to the other,
making a pool in the shallow water.
Then the beavers can build their house.
Fish and water birds may come to live
in the pool. A doe or a rat might come
to get a drink there.

When beavers want to build a dam
or a house, they look for the branch
of a big tree. They also look around
for small trees that can be cut down
little by little. Their flat tails hold
them up when they cut down trees.
They do most of the work with their
big, strong, front teeth.

Next, the beavers drag each small tree
and each branch to the water. Then
they float each branch and small tree
to the place where they want to build.

Beavers always build part of their
house above the water and part below
the water. They live in the part
of their house that is above water.
It is one big room. Its top is made
of tree bark and twigs. Beavers come
to this room to dry off. They also
stay here when it is very cold.

Beavers keep fixing their houses. They
stay in one place as long as there is
plenty to eat.

Smart beavers won't be caught with
nothing to eat. They like to eat
bark and twigs. They always keep
plenty of both under the water.

Beavers always seem to be working.
They do most of their work at night.
They always work in teams so that
they can help each other.

We can learn a lot from beavers, can't we?

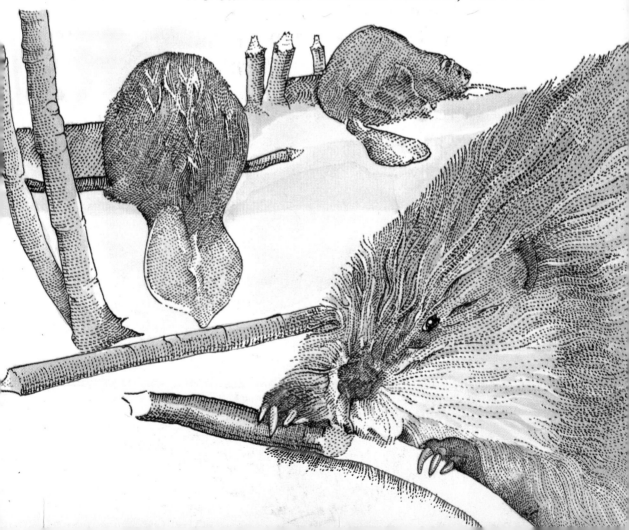

1. What do beavers look like?

2. What helps a beaver swim?

3. Where do beavers like to build their houses?

4. How do beavers cut down trees?

5. Why do beavers work in teams?

6. Do you like to work in a team? Why or why not?

7. Do you like to work alone? When might it be better to work with a team than to work alone?

PLAY BALL!

Grant, Terry, and Butch were playing ball in the lot on their street.

"It's no use," Grant said, throwing down his bat. "We're no match for the other teams. I bet if we do play, we won't score!"

Terry got up from the bench. She was mad. "What are you saying? I think you're the best batter around. And I think I'm the best pitcher."

Then Butch got up. He was mad, too! "Pitcher? Batter? What about me?" he said. "I'm a good player, too. I think I'm the best runner on the team. And I can catch and pitch, too."

All three of them started to laugh. "You're right," Grant said. "We can catch and pitch and run. I guess we are a good team. But there is one hitch. We might have some good runners and pitchers. But so far, that's about all we have!"

Butch shook his head. Terry was right. The other players weren't at the lot today. Why should they be? All the players had said they weren't much of a team now. The lot they played on had just one base. They did not have a mask or a mitt. And just one player had a sweater with no patch on it.

Butch, Terry, and Grant walked away from the lot. They were not mad now. But they were sad. What could they do? How could they get the masks, mitts, and sweaters they needed? How could they be a match for the other teams?

They were sitting on the front steps when Mrs. Singer walked out of the house. "Terry, what's the matter?" she asked. "Why do you look so sad?"

Terry told her mother. Mrs. Singer said, "If you can't get what you need, why not work for it? Each of the players on your team can do a task. You will all be paid for the tasks you do. Then you can get what your team needs."

Terry smiled at her mother. "That's the best plan we have heard yet," she said.

The next day all the players on the ball team went looking for tasks to do. In her pocket, Terry had the names of those who needed tasks done at their homes. She gave one name to each boy and girl on the team.

Grant went to see Mr. Green. He fixed the steps in back of Mr. Green's house. Terry went to see Miss Brown. She painted Miss Brown's living room. The other players pitched in, too. Bess cleaned a car. Timmy watched a baby. At the end of the day, they went back to the lot.

"Now we can get what we need,"
said Grant.

"What a switch! No more patched
sweaters," said Butch.

"We can have a third base, now,"
Terry said, laughing.

All the players gave Terry what
they got for doing their tasks. The
next day the team went shopping.
They got all the masks, mitts, bats,
balls, and sweaters that they needed.
Then they went to the lot to play ball.
But there was one hitch. The lot was
a mess. There was just one bench for
the crowd to sit on. There was no place
to put the score when there was a
home run.

"What will we do?" asked Grant. "We spent all that we had."

"Let's get started and clean this place up," Terry said.

All the players worked hard. But there was a lot to do. As they were working, Mr. Green walked by. He saw what they were doing. "It looks as if you have a long way to go. Why not let some of us help you out," he said.

The next day, Mr. Green, Miss Brown, and others came to help the team fix up the lot. They worked all day. Soon the old lot looked like a place where they could play ball.

"This is a switch," Butch said to
Mr. Green. "First, we did tasks for you.
Now you are helping us."

"But we were paid for our work,"
Grant said. "What can we do for you,
Mr. Green?"

Mr. Green laughed. "How about
winning your next game?" he said.

1. What was the matter with Terry's team?

2. What did the players do to get the things they needed?

3. What was the matter with the lot where they played?

4. Who helped the team fix up the lot?

5. Were the team's helpers paid for their work?

6. Do you think that the team will win the next game?

7. What kinds of tasks do you like to do? Do you get paid for doing any tasks?

The Best Plan

Bob	Bud	May
Bess	Dan Ford	Max
Pat	Rita	Tom

Big and Small Children

Part One

The place is a city play street.
A ball comes flying down the street.
It hits Bud and Bess. The other children
run over and form a circle around them.

Bob: Are you hurt, Bud? How about you,
Bess?

Bess: I'm not hurt, but Bud is. The ball hit
his arm. I bet there's a lump.

Pat: Let's see, Bud. Is there a lump
on your arm?

Bud: No, there's no lump. The ball didn't hit
me that hard. But look at my stamps.
They're all over the place.

The children help him pick up
the stamps.

Bess: Look at this one. It's spoiled.

Bud: She's right. It has oil on it! You
can't get oil off a stamp. It's spoiled!

85

Pat: I'll get you another, Bud. I
didn't mean to spoil your stamps.
The ball just got away.

Bess: This time you just spoiled one
of Bud's stamps. Next time you may hurt
one of us. Why do you have to play
ball here?

Bob: Where do you want us to go? Right now
we're at the very end of the street.
If you think this place has lots of oil,
you should see it down there!

*Just then, a little boy and his dog
come along. The dog barks at Bess, and
she boils over.*

86

Bess: Get that dog out of here, Dan Ford!

Dan Ford looks sad as he goes away.
The other children go back to their games.
All is well for a short time. Then
some children on bikes come riding
down the street. May almost hits Rita.

Rita: Don't you ever look where you're going?
You almost bumped into me!

May: Stop shouting. I didn't hit you, did I?

Rita: You could have! Why do you have
to ride your bikes here?

87

Max: Where should we ride them? Did you ever try to find a better place? This is the one street that's not filled with cars and trucks. What would you like us to do?

Dan Ford and his dog come running down the street and bump into Max. Max gets mad and shouts at Dan.

Max: Get out of here with that dog, or I'll . . . .

Dan: I didn't mean to bump into you!

Tom: We'll have to do SOMETHING about this street.

May: Tom is right. Maybe if we all talk it over, we'll come up with a plan. I'll get the others.

In a short time, the children have formed a circle. Dan Ford is back. He is blowing a toy horn.

Bud: Make him stop blowing that horn!
I can't hear myself think.

Max: Give me the horn, Dan.

*Dan hands the horn to Max and
starts to jump up and down.*

Max: Stop that jumping, Dan. OK, now who
has a plan?

All the children talk at one time.

Max: Hold it! Hold it! I'll be right back.

89

Part Two

*Max rides off on his bike. He comes
back with a bunch of pens and some paper.
He starts to hand out the pens and paper.*

Max: Here. Now we can each write down
a plan. Then we'll read each plan
out loud and pick the best one.

*The children sit down and start
to write. For a short time, there isn't
a sound on the street. When Max has
all the plans in his hand, he starts
to read them.*

90

Max: May wrote that this play street
should be for the small children.

Small Children: Good! That's a good plan!

Big Children: No way! Never!

Max: Bud wrote that this play street
should be for the big children.

Big Children: That's more like it!

Small Children: Never! Never!

Max looks at the next paper.

Max: This isn't another plan. It's just a bunch
of drawings!

Bess: Show them around, Max. We all
want to see.

*Max hands the drawings to Bess.
She looks at them and starts to laugh.*

Bess: This must be Dan's plan. He
can't read or write yet, so he
showed us with a drawing.

Pat: He's telling us to play ball and ride
our bikes at one time of day. He's
telling us to paint and look at stamps
at some other time of day.

Bob: You're right! There's no sun
in the drawing where we're riding bikes
and playing ball. But the sun is big
where we're painting and looking at
stamps. I like Dan's plan!

Rita: I do, too, but it needs something. Give
it to me, and I'll fix it.

Rita takes Dan's drawings. She marks them with her pen and then hands them back.

Rita: There! Now the drawings are right.
I put Dan and his horn and his dog
into each drawing. He showed us how
we can all get to do the things we like
best. Now he'll get to do the things
HE likes best.

THINK ABOUT IT

1. Who had the best plan for using
   the play street? Why?

2. What did Rita draw on Dan's drawings?

3. Why did the children need a plan?

4. What way would you find for
   all the children to play?

three

The Missing Clock

Jean Gray threw herself on the bed.

"What's wrong?" asked her older sister, Fern, in a kind voice.

"I can't find my alarm clock," said Jean.

"Ask Mom," said Fern. "She's fixing your desk lamp. Maybe she's fixing your clock, too."

"But there's nothing wrong with my clock,"
said Jean. She went off to find her mother.

Mrs. Gray was working on Jean's lamp.
When she saw her daughter's face,
she stopped. "What's wrong, Jean?" she
asked.

"I can't find my alarm clock," said Jean.
"And I must find it before three o'clock."

"Why three o'clock?" asked Mrs. Gray.

"I set it to go off then," said Jean. "Betty
will be waiting for me on Front Street.
She says I am always late. This time
I won't be."

Mrs. Gray smiled at her daughter. "When
the alarm goes off, you'll find the clock."

"Oh, Mother!" said Jean. "Stop
making fun of me. Maybe someone
turned the alarm off."

"I wasn't making fun of you, Jean," said
Mrs. Gray. "I'll help you look for the clock."

"Clock? What clock?" Mr. Gray asked
his daughter as he came into the room.

"I can't find my alarm clock!" shouted Jean.

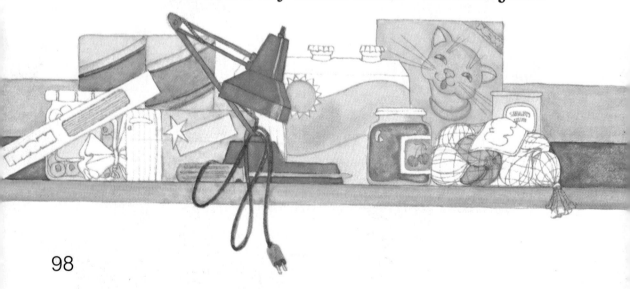

"Don't shout so, Jean," said Mr. Gray,
handing her a bag. "There's nothing wrong
with my ears."

"Oh, Dad!" said Jean. "It's just that
I need the clock."

"Maybe your alarm clock walked off
on its hands," said Mr. Gray, laughing.

"THAT'S NOT FUNNY!" said Jean
in a loud voice.

99

"OK! OK!" said Mr. Gray, holding his ears. "Why don't you ask Pam? Maybe she saw it!"

"And THAT'S not funny!" said Jean. "Pam's just a baby. She can't say ten words!"

Jean ran back to her room. "You'll help Mother and me find my clock, won't you?" she asked her older sister.

"OK! OK!" said Fern. "Just stop being so mad. Let's clear out the desk and toy chest. Maybe we'll find it there."

"We'll both help," said Mr. Gray as he and Mrs. Gray came into the room.

So Jean cleared out the toy chest, and Fern cleared out the desk. Mrs. Gray looked under pillows and behind lamps. Mr. Gray stood on a big box and looked on top of things.

"There's nothing up here but dust," said Mr. Gray as he started to sneeze. "Dust always makes me sneeze. Do you want some dust, Jean?"

"THAT'S not funny!" said Mrs. Gray.

"Well, something up here made me sneeze!" said Mr. Gray.

Just then, the alarm clock began to ring.
The Grays looked at each other. Then
they all ran into the next room.

"It's louder and clearer here!" said Fern.

"The sound IS louder and clearer in here,"
said Mr. Gray. "But where is it coming from?
This is Pam's room. SHE can't tell time!"

"Oh, Dad! Can't you stop being funny?"
asked Jean.

"Never!" said Mr. Gray.

Mrs. Gray walked over to the baby's bed
and picked her up.

"Me hear clock!" said Pam.

"We hear it, too!" said Mrs. Gray. "What
a naughty girl!" Then she began to laugh.

The others came over to see what was
so funny. They all laughed, too. There,
under Pam's pillow, was the missing clock.

"Grandma must have let her take it to bed
with her," said Mrs. Gray.

"I was right, Jean," said Mr. Gray. "You should have asked Pam about the clock. She did know where it was. She put it to bed!"

"Oh, no, Dad!" said Jean, holding her ears. But she was laughing, too.

THINK ABOUT IT

1. Why did Jean set the alarm?
2. Who looked for the clock? Where did each one look?
3. How did Jean feel when she lost the clock?
4. What would you do if you wanted to see someone on time?

Talking Hands

If you were in a far-off land, how would you ask for the food you wanted for lunch? Would you know how to ask for milk or for a roll? Could you ask for salt or a glass of water?

If you didn't already know the words for milk or roll or salt or water, what would you do? That's right! You would point to the food you wanted. You would use finger talk to get your lunch.

People all over the world talk with
their fingers. You do it yourself. What
if you want to say "OK" or "We did it!"?
You can say it with the fingers of one hand.

You can say "OK" by forming a circle
with your thumb and first finger. You
can say "We did it!" by making a **V**
with the first two fingers.

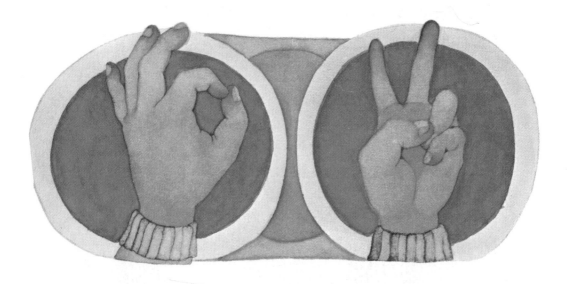

The next time you see a ball game, watch
the catcher as he or she bends down
behind the batter. The catcher will tell
the pitcher what kind of ball to pitch
by using the fingers of one hand.

If the catcher wants a slow ball, he or she may spread out three fingers and point them down. The catcher may also move the fingers as if to sprinkle something down on the dirt. For a fast ball, the catcher may point with just one finger.

People of long ago also used finger talk. Here are some of their finger-talk words.

First, cup your right hand. Then place it behind your right ear. You have said "hear" or "listen."

Next, cup both hands over your ears. You
have used finger talk to say that a noise
is too loud.

You don't have to stomp around and make
noise to show that you are mad. Just
clench your right hand into a fist. Look
at the circle formed by your thumb and
first finger. With this circle facing you,
bring your fist up to the top of your face.
Now make little circles in the air
to say that you are mad.

Clench your right hand into a fist
with your first finger pointing up. Hold
your clenched fist in front of your chest
so that you see the back of your hand.
Now bring your hand up and back
past your face. You have said "fear."

Clench your right hand into a fist. Place
the thumb of your fist below your mouth.
Now move your hand down and up,
down and up. You have said "want."

The words for wanting food, being mad, and fearing something are good words to know. You can already say them by using your voice. Now you can say them by using your fingers!

THINK ABOUT IT

1. How does a catcher tell a pitcher what kind of ball to throw?

2. How could you ask for something in a store, and not use any words?

3. How would you use finger talk to say:

It's hot!	So long!
I'm sad.	Go away!
Come here.	No noise here!

How the Finch Got Its Colors

Long ago, there was no color on the earth.
Then one spring, a rainbow could be seen
in the sky.

"Behold the rainbow," said the king
of the dull gray birds. "Follow me.
We will fly up to that thing of beauty
and bring back its bright colors."

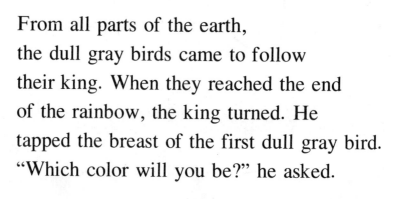

From all parts of the earth,
the dull gray birds came to follow
their king. When they reached the end
of the rainbow, the king turned. He
tapped the breast of the first dull gray bird.
"Which color will you be?" he asked.

"I will have a red breast," said the bird.
And so, he became a robin.

The king tapped the breast
of the next bird. "And you?" he asked.
"Which color will you be?"

"I will be green," said the bird. And so, there was a parrot.

The king tapped another bird. "And what color is your choice?" he asked.

"I will be brown," said the bird. And so, he became a sparrow.

The king tapped the breast of the next bird. "What is your choice?"

"I will be blue," said the bird. And so, there was a bluebird.

One by one, the dull birds came to the king.
One by one, he gave them the colors
of the rainbow. Soon there was no rainbow.
Yet the sky was still filled with its beauty.
The colors of the rainbow were now
on the birds.

The robin, parrot, sparrow, and bluebird
all held the rainbow's colors. So did
the wren, the lark, and the bald eagle.
Red and blue, green and yellow, purple,
brown, and black were the birds.

The birds turned to carry their bright beauty
back to earth. Then the rainbow of birds
became sad. For one small gray bird
was still dull.

"Why are you still dull?" asked
the king. "Why have you no bright color
for yourself? What beauty will you carry
back to earth?"

The small gray bird looked very sad.
"You gave colors to the robin, the parrot,
the sparrow, and the bluebird," he said.
"You gave colors to the wren, the lark,
and the bald eagle. All the colors
of the rainbow are used up. I will have
no beauty to carry back to earth."

"We must do something for this little one,"
the king told the other birds. "He, too,
must carry the beauty of the rainbow."

Then, one by one, the other birds went
to the little dull bird. One by one, they
gave him colors from THEIR bright breasts.

116

Soon the dull gray bird was a rainbow
of colors. Red and blue, green and
yellow, black, brown, and purple
were all mixed on its breast.

"Behold the finch!" said the king.
"The finch will carry all the colors
of the rainbow back to earth!"

THINK ABOUT IT

1. Where did the birds fly to get
   their bright colors?

2. What color did the parrot want?

3. How did the birds help the
   small bird who was still dull?

4. A little cub was cold and needed
   fur. A fox, a dog, and a beaver
   wanted to help. What could they do?

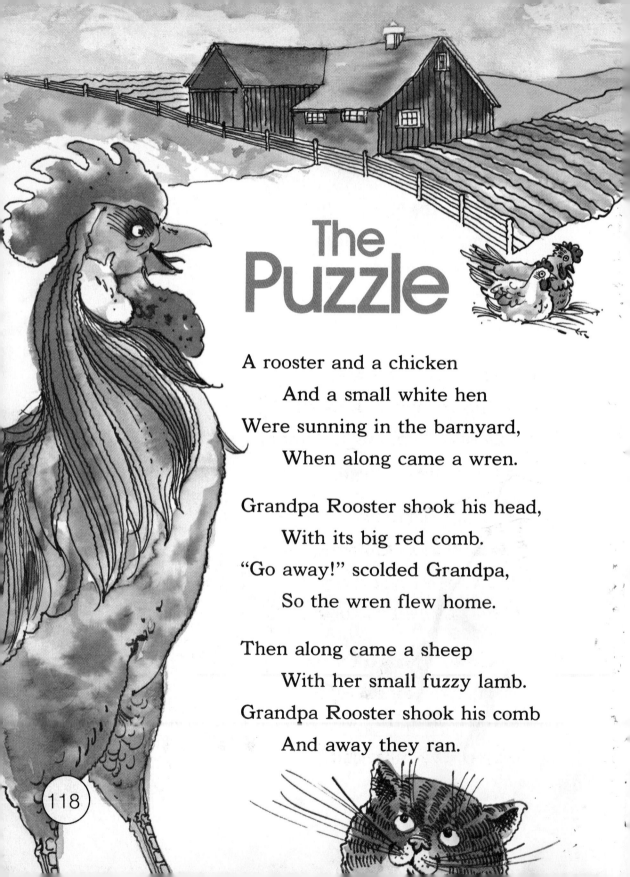

The Puzzle

A rooster and a chicken
    And a small white hen
Were sunning in the barnyard,
    When along came a wren.

Grandpa Rooster shook his head,
    With its big red comb.
"Go away!" scolded Grandpa,
    So the wren flew home.

Then along came a sheep
    With her small fuzzy lamb.
Grandpa Rooster shook his comb
    And away they ran.

Soon a small happy kitten,
　　To the barnyard prowled.
Grandpa Rooster shook his comb,
　　And the kitten howled.

Then a little yellow bee
　　To the barnyard came.
Grandpa Rooster ran away.
　　The others did the same!

"It's a puzzle," buzzed the bee.
　　"Why did they all run?
All I came to do was play.
　　Why can't I have fun?"

The Old House

Part One

There's a big old house a few streets
from where I live. Every little thing
about that house is ugly. My dad says
it's only an old house that no one
has lived in for years. But I think
someone or something must live there.
People always talk about hearing
funny sounds there or seeing lights.

120

My friend Barry says it's the kind of house that writers are always writing about. Barry wants to be a writer someday. So he and I had talked about going over there to get a better look at the place. But we never did.

One day, Barry and I had nothing to do, so we took a walk. Our friends always go to Mr. Lamb's candy store. We headed that way, too. When we got there, we didn't see anyone we knew.

Barry asked the woman who works for Mr. Lamb for a candy bar. While the woman was getting the candy, I went outside. After a while, Barry came out.

"Say! This might be the time to get
a better look at that ugly old house,"
said Barry. "What do you think?"

I didn't much like the thought. But I
knew that Barry wanted me to go with him.
So I just kind of went along.

Barry and I walk pretty fast. In no time
at all we were standing only a few feet
from the house. It was a cloudy day,
so it was pretty dark. We listened, but we
couldn't hear a sound. When something
brushed against me, I jumped.

"It's only a black cat," said Barry. He
laughed and pulled me along. "Come on,
let's knock and see if anyone is home!"

"Don't be funny!" I said, pulling him behind a big tree. "You can't just go up and knock! Let's stand here for a while and see what happens."

"Why are you talking in such a low voice?"
asked Barry.

"Why are YOU talking in a low voice?"
I asked. Then we both laughed
out loud!

The sound of our laughing wasn't very
funny in the dark. I felt cold all over,
and I could feel a knot in my insides.

"Maybe we ought to go," I said.

"You can go if you want to," said Barry.
"I want to stay and see what happens."

I didn't know what he thought was going
to happen. Maybe he was waiting
for some bike riders to come by. I sat down
against a tree and took out a cake I had saved.

I always eat when I'm knotted up inside.
I had just put the cake in my mouth
when I looked up and saw a light. Then
I just couldn't get that cake down!

"What's the matter with you?" asked Barry.
"You look like a fish!"

Part Two

After what felt like a year, the cake
went down. "Didn't you see it?" I asked.
"There's a light in the house."

"I didn't see a thing," said Barry.

"There it is again," I said. "See it!"

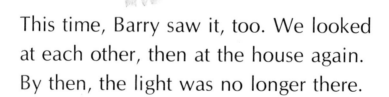

This time, Barry saw it, too. We looked
at each other, then at the house again.
By then, the light was no longer there.

Just then, there was a loud BANG!
You never heard anything like that bang!

I jumped up and started to run. I
didn't know if Barry was behind me or not.
I wasn't about to stop to find out.

126

I was running hard, with my head down.
My insides were all knotted up again.
When I looked up, the street was all
fuzzy. Then something flashed by me.

"It's after us!" I thought. "It must be
some mover. We'll never get away."
But then, I saw that it was only Barry.
I almost didn't know him. His face was
all knotted up. His feet were going
so fast that I thought he would fall!

By the time I saw Barry again, we were both
back in town. He was standing outside a store
on Bank Street. There were lots of people around.

"Why did you run?" I asked.

"Me? How about you?" he said, laughing.
"I heard that loud noise and saw you start
to run. So I ran, too."

"What movers! Did we ever run!" I said.

The two of us began to laugh. We laughed
so hard, we had to sit down right there
in the center of Bank Street. Every time
I stopped laughing, I would think of the look
on Barry's face as he ran by me. Then I
would laugh again!

After a while, we began walking home.
"What do you think it was?" I asked.

"I don't know," said Barry. "But
someone was telling me about this cabin
on the beach . . . ."

I didn't stay to hear what was coming next.
Let Barry go see the cabin. I'M writing about
the ugly old house!

THINK ABOUT IT

1. How did the girl feel when she and Barry went
   to the old house?
2. Why did the children go to the old house?
3. Why couldn't the girl get the cake down?
4. What do you do when you feel the way
   the girl did?

four

THE VOICE FROM THE DEEP

Part One

"Don't step on that crack in the sidewalk!"
Joe March called. "You'll spoil your luck.
You may drop the dollar your father gave you."

Joe's friend Wally just laughed and ran on.
The boys were on their way to the stores
to find a box for Wally's father.

"Let's swing over to Cross Street and
try the food stores first," said Joe. "Turn
at the corner. Then we'll swing back
this way. But watch those cracks!"

"What is THAT?" asked Wally as they
turned the corner. He was pointing
at a funny-looking slide at the back
of a big green truck. The truck stood in front
of the Dollar Food Store.

The boys walked over to the slide.
It ran from the back of the truck
to a big open space in the sidewalk.
Two sets of rollers ran along the slide
and down into the opening.

"I never saw anything like that before,"
said Joe, looking down into the opening.

"Do you think anyone is down there?"
asked Wally.

"Why don't you call down and find out?"
asked Joe.

"Hello down there!" called Wally.

"HELLO UP THERE!" boomed a voice from below.

"There's someone down there!" said Wally. "Who are you?"

"THE VOICE FROM THE DEEP," boomed the voice.

"The deep? The deep what?" called Wally.

"THE DEEP CELLAR!" the voice boomed.

"What are you doing down there?" called Joe.

"WORKING FOR DOLLAR'S!" boomed the voice.

"Here it comes!" said another voice.

"Anytime!" shouted the voice from the deep.

Turning, the boys saw a man on the truck. The man opened the collar of his shirt. Then he picked up a big box. The box was VERY big. They could see the man's arms swell as he picked it up.

"Just look at his arms swell," said Joe as the man put the box on the rollers.

The box slid along the sidewalk on the rollers and into the cellar. "GOT IT!" shouted the voice from the deep.

RUCKING

"What does he do with it?" Joe asked
the man with the open collar.

"He catches it as it comes off the rollers,"
said the man. "He watches the rollers. Then
he catches each box as it comes off."

The man put box after box on the rollers.
Soon all the boxes from the truck were on their
way into the cellar.

Part Two

"It looks as if the cellar is eating all those boxes!" said Wally, laughing.

"Why don't you ask the voice from the deep if you can have one?" said Joe.

"Hello down there," shouted Wally. "Can I have one of your boxes for my father?"

"SURE! ONE BOX COMING UP!" boomed the voice. "JUST WAIT. I'LL OPEN ONE UP AND TAKE OUT THE CANS."

Then the boys heard the noise of some cans rolling around in the cellar.

"LOOK OUT!" boomed the voice. "HERE COMES YOUR BOX!"

The boys jumped back as a small box
came flying up from the cellar. Joe
picked it up and pointed to the words
on the side. "This would be a good place
to keep my new pup," he said, laughing.
"See if the voice will give you another one
so that we can swap."

"Thanks for the box!" Wally shouted.
"May I have another one so that I can swap
with my friend? He has a new dog!"

The voice laughed. "WHY DO YOU NEED
A BOX?" it boomed.

"I don't," said Wally. "But my father does."

"IS THIS ONE OK?" boomed the voice.
Another box came flying up from the deep.

The boys picked it up and read it. "Just
look at that!" said Joe. "This is a good box
for your father. His name is Frank!"

"Thanks a lot," Wally shouted
into the opening.

"COME BACK ANYTIME," boomed the voice.

On the way home, the boys looked
at the boxes. "That voice from the deep
sure knew a lot about us," said Wally.

"You can say that again," said Joe.

THINK ABOUT IT

1. Why did Joe say, "Don't step on the cracks"?
2. Why did Wally want a box? Why did Joe want a box?
3. Why was the first box a good one for a dog? Why was the other box good for Wally's father?
4. Who was "the voice from the deep"?
5. If you needed a box, where would you get one?

A Snail Takes a Walk

A snail has been out walking.
I see its shining track
Weave like a silver ribbon
Across our porch and back.

The other snails are sleeping
Out in the flower bed,
But this one got up early
And took a walk instead.

The Lesson

Once, I learned this lesson,
I never knew before.
Some people get up early,
To bring goods to the store.

Into the lonely city,
Through freezing rain and snow,
Along the long dark roadways
The trucks and wagons go.

Since most of us are sleeping,
We never hear their hum,
As through our still, dark city,
The lonely truckers come.

THE GENIE OF THE LAMP

Long ago and far away, there lived
a gentle old woman and a gentle old man.
These two gentle people had nothing
in the world but the house in which they lived.
Each morning, the man went fishing so that
there would be food on the table.

Each night, when the man brought the fish home, the woman would weigh them. She would sell those that weighed over a pound. She would boil those that weighed under a pound. And so they lived, year after year after year.

Then one morning, when the man went fishing, he caught only huge rocks and stones. All day long he fished but caught nothing to take home.

Just as the man was ready to give up, he pulled in a small dirty lamp. "There will be no fish to weigh tonight," he thought. "But maybe we can sell the lamp and get some food."

When she saw the lamp, the woman was very sad. She knew they would feel hunger that night. Since she didn't want to hurt the man's feelings, she started to clean the lamp.

"You will do better in the morning," she said. Then she took the top off the lamp.

At once there was a huge purple cloud. Out of the cloud came a huge purple genie.

Since they were gentle people, the man and the woman were filled with fear.

"Who— Who— Who are you?" asked the woman.

"I AM THE GENIE OF THE LAMP!" boomed the purple genie in a voice deep with anger.

"Where do you come from?" asked
the man.

"I COME FROM ANOTHER AGE AND
ANOTHER PLACE," boomed the genie.
"I HAVE BEEN INSIDE THAT LAMP
FOR AGES AND AGES AND AGES.
GET ME SOME FOOD!"

"We have no food," said the woman.

At this, the genie's face wrinkled with anger.

"THEN I WILL EAT YOU ALL UP!"
he boomed.

"Please!" said the woman. "I urge you
to be kind. We have done you no harm."

"THEN BRING ME FOOD!" boomed the genie,
pounding the table in anger.

The gentle old man did not feel
very brave. But he knew that he must do
something to make the genie go away.
He wrinkled up his face and shouted
at the genie.

"Is this any way to thank us for setting
you free? A real genie would have thanked
us with silver and gold! A real genie
would have thanked us with huge boxes
of gems!"

"SO!" boomed the genie. "A REAL GENIE
WOULD THANK YOU WITH SILVER AND GOLD
AND GEMS, WOULD HE!"

With that, a huge purple cloud
filled the air. When the cloud went away,
a chest of silver and gold and gems
stood beside the table.

"NOW WHO SAYS I'M NOT REAL?" boomed
the genie.

The man was still trying to be brave. He wrinkled up his face again. "I do!" he said. "I still say you are not a real genie. You look more like a giant!"

The genie turned to the woman. He boomed, "DO YOU THINK I LOOK MORE LIKE A GIANT THAN A GENIE?"

"I'm not sure," said the woman. "If you're a real genie, how come you stayed in the lamp for ages? How come you needed me to let you out?"

"BE STILL!" boomed the genie. "EVEN A GENIE CAN'T GET OUT OF A LAMP WITHOUT SOME HELP!"

"But you can't even get back in," said the woman. "You weigh far too much to fit through that small opening in the lamp."

"YOU'RE SURE OF THAT, ARE YOU?" boomed the genie.

Again, a huge purple cloud filled the air. When the cloud went away, so did the genie!

"NOW WHAT DO YOU SAY?" boomed the voice of the genie from inside the lamp.

"Now I am sure!" said the woman, as the man put the top back on the lamp. "I am sure that you are a real genie and not just a giant. I am also sure that we will never take the top off that lamp again! Even if you urge us to!"

"I am sure of that, too!" said the man. "And I am sure that we will never feel hunger again."

"Let me out! Let me out!" urged the genie. This time, his voice was not booming at all.

THINK ABOUT IT

1. What did the gentle old man do to get food?
2. How did the genie show he was a real genie?
3. How did the woman get the genie to go back into the lamp?
4. Do you think the man and the woman ever took the top off the lamp again? Would you? Why or why not?

HOW DOES YOUR GARDEN GROW?

OAK TREE

ACORN

All plants and flowers grow from seeds.
Seeds will grow into new plants just like
the plants from which you take them. If you
plant the seeds from a yellow sunflower,
you will get more sunflowers with yellow
petals. If you plant an acorn, the seeds
of an oak tree, you will get an oak tree.

153

Seeds are planted in many ways.
Some just fall to the ground and grow
into new plants. Others are planted
by people. Squirrels also plant seeds.
The squirrel likes to eat acorns and will
sometimes hide them in the ground!

The picture below shows how a new plant
grows. Start with "Seed" and you will see
part of what happens.

Growing oak trees from seeds takes a long time. Growing bean plants from seeds is much faster. Let's take a look at a seed from a bean plant.

The bean seed in the picture below has been cut in half. Here you can see both the inside and the outside parts of the seed.

BEAN SEED

The outside part of the bean seed is tough. This tough part of the seed is its skin. Inside the skin, you can see the part of the seed where the food is stored. A new plant will grow through the tough skin.

Most plants and flowers grow
in outside gardens. They will also grow
in other places. If you know how to do it,
you can grow a bean plant inside.

The best place to grow an inside garden
is in a room with lots of sunshine. Most
plants and all flowers need light to grow.

If you place the bean seeds in some dirt,
the new plant will start to grow. Soon
the stem will force its way up through the dirt
to the sunshine above. The roots will spread
through the rough ground and grow, too.

You know that a plant forces its way
through the dirt so that it will get enough light.
But plants need more than light to help them
grow. They also need enough water.

If the bean plant gets enough light and enough water, you will soon see a small green leaf on its stem. After a few days, you will see another leaf and then another. Soon your plant will start to grow its own beans.

Would you like to grow your own garden?
Here is how to do it. You will need
a seed, a cup or pot, dirt, water, and
a sunny place.

1. Put dirt in the pot.
2. Push a seed into the dirt.
3. Put some water over the seed.
4. Place dirt over the seed and water again.
5. Put the pot in a sunny place and water
   every day.

Soon you will have your own inside garden!

THINK ABOUT IT

1. What do you plant to get flowers?

2. What do flowers need to grow?

3. Take two plants. Put one in a sunny place. Put the other in a dark place. Give them both water. Watch them for ten days. Write down what you see.

4. Take two plants. Put them both in a sunny place. Water one. Do not give the other one any water. Watch them for ten days. Write down what you see.

Something for Tony

Part One

Tony read the letter over and over.

"What great news!" he shouted. He ran to find his mother. "Mother! I'm the winner! Listen to this letter."

Dear Tony,

We're happy to tell you
that you are the winner
of our paper's Fresh Air Trip
to the country.

You'll be staying at
the home of Mr. and Mrs. Brown
and their son, Ray. They are
all very pleased that you will
be staying with them for
the summer.

Please write and tell them why
you want to stay in the country.

Have a nice summer.

Wally Bank
(The City Paper)

"That is good news, dear," said
Tony's mother. "You must write to the Browns
today."

In a few days, Tony had a letter
from the Browns. He read it to his mother.

Dear Tony,
We're happy to know
that you'll be staying
with us this summer.
We know you'll like
the country. We have
two ducks, three chickens,
and a cow that gives
fresh milk every day.
Our young son Ray
is just about your age.
He has something special
for you.
We'll be waiting for
your train.
Your friends,
The Browns

"Wasn't it nice of the Browns to write?"
said Tony's mother. "And isn't it nice
that they have a young son your age?"

"Yes," said Tony. "But what do you think the something special is? Do you think we'll like each other? I can't wait to get my first sniff of fresh country air!"

"You'll sniff it soon enough," said Tony's mother. "I don't know what the something special is. But I'm sure you'll like the Browns. I KNOW they will like you."

At last, the great day came for Tony's trip to the country. At first, the train rolled along above the streets. Looking down, Tony could see lots of cars. Looking up, he could see puffs of gray smoke. The puffs of smoke were coming from some of the houses.

Part Two

After a while, the city streets and
the puffs of smoke were no more. Tony
began to see lots of grass and trees.

At last, the train came to Tony's stop.
"Tony! Tony!" called a young boy as Tony
got off the train.

"Let me help you with your bag, Tony,"
said a kind-looking man.

"We're the Browns, dear," said a woman
who was standing beside the man. Behind them
was a farm truck.

"How did you know me?" asked Tony.

"You were the first one off the train," said Ray. "And you were sniffing the air as if you never smelled it before! Come on, Tony. I can't wait to show you . . ."

"Hold on, Ray," said Mr. Brown. "Give Tony a little time. He will get to see things for himself."

"Come on, Tony," said Ray as he hopped into the truck. "We'll ride in the back."

"I never rode in a truck before," said Tony.

"Just wait," said Ray, laughing. "A truck isn't the only thing you'll ride . . ."

"Ray!" shouted Mr. Brown from the front of the truck.

"Is your dad mad about something?" asked Tony.

"No," said Ray, laughing. "He just doesn't want me to tell."

"Tell what?" asked Tony.

"You'll see pretty soon now," said Ray.

"Be home in time for lunch, boys," called Mrs. Brown as the boys jumped down from the truck.

"OK," called Ray as they ran off.

Tony ran along beside Ray. "Are we going to see the chickens and ducks and cow now?" he asked.

"Yes," said Ray as they came to a small red barn. "I'll get you a drink of fresh milk first. Then we'll see the other things."

"Can I touch her?" asked Tony when he saw the cow.

"Sure you can touch her," said Ray. "Just be sure you stand up front. She likes to see who's touching her. Wait for me here. I'll be right back."

When Ray came back, he was riding a small brown-and-white pony.

"Isn't he great, Tony?" he asked. "When we got your letter, we read how much you wanted to ride a real pony. He's your something special to ride all summer."

"A real pony!" said Tony. "He sure IS something special. Now I KNOW this will be a great summer!"

THINK ABOUT IT

1. What did Tony win?
2. How did Tony get to the country?
3. What was the special thing for Tony?
4. What do you think Tony saw on the farm?
5. What would be something special for you to do in the summer?

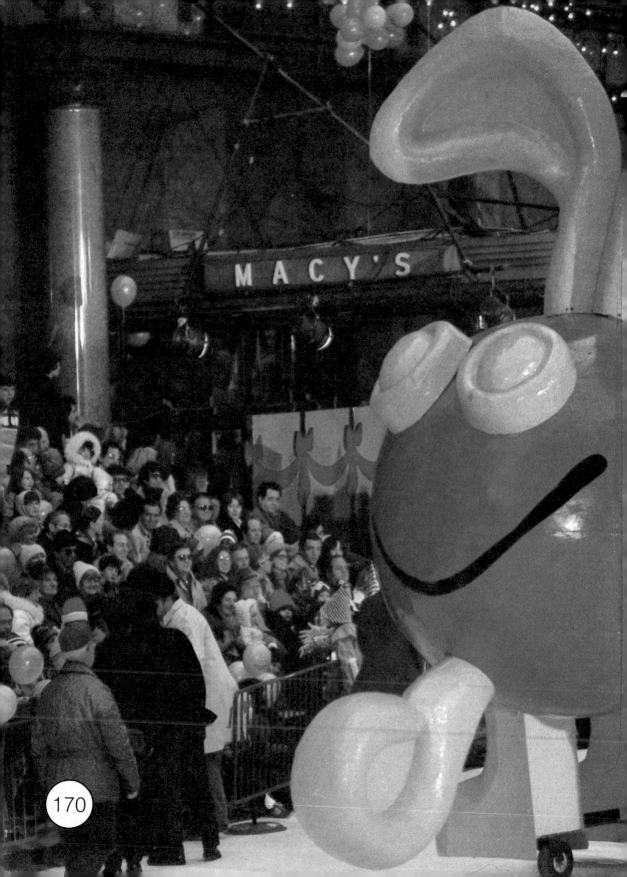

five

WORK
FOR WILLY

Willy, the giraffe, sighed a big sigh. "No other animal is as sad as I," he said to himself. "Oh, how I wish I weren't a giraffe."

Willy stretched his long neck up high
to the top of a tall tree. Then he picked
a green leaf from one of the branches.

Willy sighed again. "All I ever do is eat,"
he said. "Eat! Eat! Eat! I'm tired of eating.
I'm tired of doing nothing but eat!"

Willy moved to another tall tree.
Stretching way up high, he picked another
green leaf from another branch. "If I didn't
eat, I would have nothing to do," he said.

Willy could see the zebras on the other side
of the stream. They were looking for food.

"I have always wanted to LOOK for food," Willy said to himself. "But all I ever have to do to find it is stretch my neck. I never have to travel through the tall grass. I never have to swim through streams or fly through the air. All I ever have to do is stretch out my neck to any tall tree."

Willy sighed. "All the other animals have to travel around to find food," he said. "But not me. I'm so sad. No other animal is as sad as I."

Just then, Willy sniffed something funny
in the air. "Can that be a fire?" he asked.

Willy stretched out his long neck
as far as he could and looked around.
Far away, on the other side of the stream,
he saw a big grass fire.

"I must tell the other animals,"
thought Willy. "They must get away
from the fire."

"Fire! Fire!" he called. But
the other animals couldn't hear him.

"I must cross the stream," thought Willy.
He took a giant step and landed
on the other side of the stream.

"Fire! Fire!" he called to the zebras.
"Can't you see the fire?"

"No," said the zebras. "We have short necks. We can't see as far as you can, Willy."

"Can't you smell the fire?" asked Willy.

"No," said the zebras. "We can't smell the way you can, Willy."

Willy was tired, but he ran to tell the big cats about the fire.

"Fire! Fire!" he called to the big cats, who were in the brush. "Can't you see the fire?"

"We can't see as far as you can, Willy," said the big cats. "We have short necks."

"You must all move across the stream," Willy told the other animals. "The fire can't cross the water. You'll be fine on the other side of the stream."

The cats moved to the other side of the stream. "It's a good thing Willy has a long neck," they said. "We ought to hire him to watch out for fires! He can travel from place to place to look for them."

"Yes," said the zebras. "It's a good thing he can smell fire and clear a stream in one giant step. You're right. We should hire him to watch out for fires!"

So the other animals hired Willy to watch out for fires. Willy was a very happy giraffe. At last, he had something to do besides eat!

THINK ABOUT IT

1. Why was Willy sad?
2. How did Willy show he was sad?
3. How did Willy help the other animals?
4. How did Willy help himself by helping the other animals?
5. Write about a pony who doesn't like being so small.

SUNTIME

Have you ever asked some friends to be
guests in your home? How did your guests
know when it was time to be there?
Did they look at a wristwatch or a clock?
Or did they just guess the time?

Looking at wristwatches and clocks is
the best and fastest way to tell time.
But, before we had such things, people
used the sun as a guide in telling time.

When the sun was right overhead, they
knew it was the middle of the day. They
could keep guessing the time by seeing
how far down the sun had gone.

One sunny morning, a man happened
to look at the ground. He saw that
his shadow pointed away from the sun.
He watched his shadow for a long time
and saw that it changed in size. As
the sun got higher, his shadow got smaller.
By the time the sun was overhead,
the man had almost no shadow at all.

"How strange!" he thought. "My shadow ranges in size from long to short. It is longest early in the morning. It is shortest in the middle of the day when the sun is right overhead."

After a while, the man went to sleep for an hour or two. When he got up, he saw another strange thing. His shadow had not only changed size. It had moved from one side of him to the other!

As the hours went by, the man saw his shadow change size again and again. It ranged from long to short to long again!

One morning, there was a haze. The man saw almost no shadow. As the hours went by, the haze got thicker. Soon the man saw no shadow at all. It was gone.

"That is another strange thing," thought the man. "One cannot see a shadow when there is a haze in the air!"

The man now knew about sun shadows. He knew that he could use these shadows as a guide for telling time.

When guests came to call, the man
told them what he had learned.
Soon someone made the first sundial.

The first sundial was called a "shadow
stick." The dial was a stone bar.
A big **T** sat across the top of the dial.

As the morning sun came over the **T,**
the shadow of the **T** fell on the dial.
The place where the shadow fell
was called "suntime." At noon, the stick
was turned so that the shadow of the **T**
would still fall on the dial.

In the morning, suntime on the shadow
stick showed the hours BEFORE noon.
In the middle of the day, after the stick
was turned, suntime showed the hours
AFTER noon.

Many years went by before people used
metal for sundials. Metal sundials ranged
in size, but most were round. These round
metal sundials can still be seen today.
They are still being used as a guide
for telling time.

1. How did people tell time before there were clocks?

2. Where is the sun in the middle of the day?

3. What was the first sundial called?

4. Why is a clock better than a sundial?

5. Have you ever had to tell time without using a clock? How did you do it?

Down Silver Streams

Each night I travel to strange places.
I eat strange foods and see strange faces.
I float on boats down silver streams.
These things all happen in my dreams.

I travel on land and through the air.
While deep into sleep, I go everywhere.
I take very long trips into space.
Yes, I can go to most any place.

Some nights I'm fast, as fast as can be.
I tear through the air just like a bee.
And when I'm strong, my cough or sneeze
Will be enough to start a breeze.

Like the big giraffe, I can be tall.
Like the tiny ant, I can be small.
I can be young; I can be old.
I can wear both silver and gold.

Anything I can picture I can be,
A lion, a bear, even a bee.
It's not hard to do what I do.
It's something you can do. Yes, you!

All you must do is hop into bed.
Then, with a pillow under your head,
Turn off each bad thought of the day,
And let happy dreams take you away.

Rumpelstiltskin

Part One

Once upon a time, there was a miller
with a young daughter. One day, the king
came to their town. Wishing to please
the king, the miller told him that his daughter
could spin straw into gold.

"That would please me," said the king.
"Bring your daughter to me tomorrow. If
she cannot do as you say, things will go
hard with you."

The miller was filled with sorrow. "My daughter cannot spin straw into gold," he said. "Oh, why did I say she could?"

The next day, the king took the miller's daughter to a room filled with straw. "Do not tarry!" he said. "You must turn this straw into gold by tomorrow."

When the king left, the young woman began to weep. She could not spin straw into gold. She was filled with sorrow.

"Hello," said a voice. "Why do you weep?"

Looking up, she saw an ugly little man. "I must turn this straw into gold by tomorrow," said the young woman.

"What will you give me to spin it on my wheel?" asked the ugly little man.

"I will give you my gold pin," she said.

The little man plunged into work.
By morning, the room was filled with gold.

The king was quite pleased to see
the gold, but he wanted more. He took
the young woman to a room filled
with still more straw.

"Spin, and be quick about it!" said
the king. "Turn this straw into gold,
or things will go hard with your father."

The young woman began to weep. Once
again, the ugly little man came to her.

"What will you give me to spin THIS straw
into gold on my wheel?" he asked.

"My gold ring," she said.

At once, the ugly little man plunged
into his spinning. By morning, the straw
was gone. The room was filled with gold.

Part Two

Again, the king was quite pleased, but he wanted even more gold. He took the young woman to another room filled with straw.

"Spin this straw into gold. Then I will marry you, and you will be queen," said the king.

As soon as the king left, the ugly man came back. "What will you give me if I spin THIS straw into gold?" he asked.

"I have nothing left," said the woman.

"No," said the ugly little man. "But you are about to marry the king. When you are queen, will you give me your first baby?"

"Yes! Yes!" said the young woman. "Just be quick and spin the straw into gold."

The ugly little man plunged right into work. By morning, the straw was gone. The room was filled with gold.

The king was very pleased, and soon the young woman became queen.

In time, the queen had a fine baby girl. Then one day the ugly little man came to see the queen.

"The baby is mine," he said. "You told me you would give me your first baby."

"I will give you all the gold I have and all that I can borrow," she said.

"I do not want gold. I want your baby," said the ugly little man. "But I am not a hard man. I will give you three days. If you can guess my name by then, I will not take the baby."

When the little man had gone, the queen
sent her fastest rider to the far fringes
of the land.

"Bring me all the boys' names you hear,"
she said. "Do not tarry. I must guess the
right name in three days."

Then the queen wrote down all the boys'
names she could think of. The next day,
she showed them to the man.

"That is not my name," he said as he read
each name. "I'll be back tomorrow."

When the man left, the queen asked everyone to write down boys' names. The next day, she showed them to the man.

"Not one of these names is right!" said the ugly little man. "You have one day left to guess my name."

The next day, the queen's rider came back from the far fringes of the land. "These are all the names I could find," he said, handing her a paper. "But as I rode through the woods, I saw a house. Before the house was a fire. And before the fire sat an ugly little man. As he sat, he sang a song."

Today I sit, tomorrow I bake.
And after that, the baby I take.
Her mother, the queen, will not be
  to blame.
For who could guess
  RUMPELSTILTSKIN is my name?

That night, the queen showed the paper with the boys' names to the ugly man.

"My name is not here," said the man.

Then the queen smiled. "Is your name Rumpelstiltskin?" she asked.

"You cannot know! You cannot know!" shouted the ugly little man. He jumped up and down. Harder and harder he jumped. At last, he jumped right through the ground and was never seen again.

1. What was the first thing the miller's daughter gave to the ugly little man?

2. What was the next thing she gave to the ugly little man?

3. How do you think the young woman felt about having to spin straw into gold?

4. What did the miller tell the king? Why did he say that?

5. What would you give to someone who could turn stones into anything you would like?

CITY FISHING

Joy Miller   **Mike**   **Ward**

Ray   **Ann**   **Emmy**

Part One

It's a warm, sunny morning. Joy Miller is on her way to the store for her mother. She sees some of her friends and calls to them.

Joy: Who wants to come to the store with me? My mom is painting our back porch, and she needs two small brushes.

198

Ray: Porches are hard to paint with a brush.
Why doesn't she use a roller?

Joy: She used a roller on the floor. But
you can't use a roller on the trim.
The paint gets all over. I've got
three quarters. Who wants to come?

*Joy flips a quarter into the air
and catches it between her fingers.*

Mike: I can't. I've got a drum lesson.

Ann: I've got to make lunch for my sister.

Ward: Emmy and I will go if it won't take long. We've got to be home by one o'clock.

Emmy: Good! I like going to the store.

Joy groans and stops flipping the quarter.

Joy: Does she HAVE to come?

Ward: Well, I've got to watch her. So if I come, she comes, too.

Joy: Well, OK. But we've got to walk fast, Emmy. I can't wait around.

Emmy: I will! I will! I'll walk fast. You won't have to wait for me! I'll even run!

Joy smiles. Then turning, she starts down the street. Ward goes with her. Emmy, who is playing with a yo-yo, walks between them.

Joy: It's too warm to run. Just keep up. I've got to get back fast. Mom is waiting for those brushes.

*At the next corner, the children wait
for the light. Emmy starts to wind up
her yo-yo. Joy flips a quarter high in the air
and catches it.*

Ward: I'm warning you. You'll drop that quarter
down a drain or something.

Joy: Never! I've been flipping things for so long
I never miss.

Joy flips the quarter again. This time she misses. It rolls into the street, and she and Ward run after it.

Ward: Quick! Get it before it rolls down the drain!

They are too late. The quarter has already rolled down the drain. Joy groans and covers her face with both hands.

Ward: I warned you! You've lost the quarter!
Emmy: He warned you!

Part Two

Joy looks at Emmy, who keeps
playing with her yo-yo.

Joy: Now what am I going to do? I won't have
enough for two brushes without that quarter.

Emmy: You'll just have to go home and get
another one.

Joy: I don't think my mom would like that.

All three children bend over the drain.

Ward: I see it! Maybe I can reach it with this.

*Ward gets down and puts a stick
between the bars of the drain cover.
Up, down, up, down goes Emmy's yo-yo
over his head. Ward looks up at her.*

Ward: Will you get that thing away
from my head, Emmy!
Joy: Never mind the yo-yo. Did you
get the quarter?
Ward: No, the stick isn't long enough to reach it.
Too bad that yo-yo can't help us get that quarter!

*Ward laughs and reaches for the yo-yo.
Emmy clutches the string and jumps back.*

Joy: Say! I just had a thought! Who has some gum?
Ward: Gum? Your mom is waiting for brushes.
You've lost a quarter. And all you can think of
is GUM!
Emmy: I don't have any. But I'll go get some, Joy.
Joy: Thanks, Emmy.

Emmy runs off to get the gum.

Ward: What do you want gum for?

Joy: To go fishing. We need something sticky.

In no time at all, Emmy is back. Joy puts the gum in her mouth. Then she rolls the wad of gum into a ball.

Joy: Now let me have your yo-yo, Emmy.

Emmy clutches her yo-yo.

Emmy: No! Never!

Joy: Please, Emmy. The gum is getting sticky!

*Emmy winds up the yo-yo and hands it
to Joy. Joy sticks the wad of gum
on the side of the yo-yo. She drops it
between the bars of the drain cover.*

Ward: I see what you're trying to do!

*Ward gets down beside Joy and
watches her. Up and down goes
the yo-yo. At last, the quarter
sticks to the gum. Joy hands
the yo-yo to Ward, and she takes
the quarter off.*

Ward: Great going, Joy!

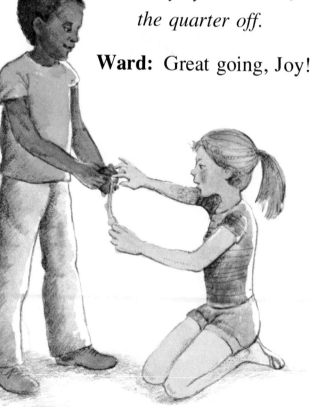

Emmy: But look at my yo-yo. It has gum
all over it!

Joy: That's OK, Emmy! I'll clean it off.
I'll even give you my best yo-yo!

THINK ABOUT IT

1. What was Joy's mother doing?

2. Who went to the store with Joy?

3. What did Ward warn Joy about?

4. Do you think Joy wanted Emmy to go along?
Why do you think so?

5. Think of a way to get a kite down from a tree
without going up after it.

six

THE CHIEF PRIVATE EYE

Part One

Brenda was out of bed before her alarm clock went off. She couldn't believe what day it was! She looked the same today. She felt the same today. But she knew that today was going to be very special, because today she was ten years old.

She dressed and ran down to see what her sister Jenny was cooking. Her mother and father were due at work. But they had left something for her on the table in the living room. Her sister was waiting for her.

"Well," Jenny said. "How do you feel today? Aren't you happy?"

"Yes, I am," Brenda said with a smile. Then she opened the box from her mother and father. Inside the box was a red sweater. She put it on and ran outside. She wanted to show her new sweater to her friends Jean and Mary right away.

The wind was blowing hard as Brenda walked down the street. All at once she stopped smiling. Her footsteps dragged. Brenda wouldn't see Jean or Mary today. They lived far away from her now. Brenda had moved to her new home last summer. She knew she wouldn't see her old friends for a long time.

It wasn't true that Brenda was happy. Because she missed her old friends so much, she felt very lonely. Brenda walked home. As she opened her front door, she saw a piece of paper. It said, "This is your first clue. Be a good private eye today and your dream will come true." At the end of the paper was a ten printed in red.

Brenda looked at the sheet of paper again and again. Who could the sender be? What did the clue mean? Did her big sister know something about this?

"Jenny, did you put a piece of paper under the front door for me?" asked Brenda.

"No, I didn't," Jenny said. "I've been here in the living room looking at these pictures all morning."

Brenda went up to her room. She
didn't see Jenny smile as she picked
up her book of pictures again.

In her room, Brenda looked
at the sheet of paper. She was thinking
about the clue.

"I know," she said, jumping up
from her bed. "Today I am ten years old.
I can't prove it now, but I'm sure this clue
has something to do with that. If I only
knew who wrote it."

Brenda was on her way to tell her sister about the clue when she heard a knock at the door. She ran to the front door as fast as she could. Did she hear someone laughing outside?

"I bet this has something to do with the paper I found under the door," she thought. As she opened the door, Brenda could see a girl running down the front walk.

"Wait," she called after her. "Whoever you are, I want to talk to you."

Part Two

But the girl did not stop running. Brenda looked down and saw another sheet of paper. It said, "A good private eye always looks for more clues."

"Well," thought Brenda. "Whoever wrote the first clue must have another clue for me to find. Where could it be?"

Brenda looked everywhere. First, she looked in her room. There was nothing under her pillow or in her jacket pocket. Next, she looked between her books. She had a special hiding place in back of a book called "The Best Indian Chief." But there was nothing there!

"Let me think about this," she said
to herself. "Just because I found
two letters, I can't prove I will find
another one. I know the sender of the
letters has another clue for me. But
just what should I be looking for?"

Brenda was sitting on her bed looking
very puzzled, when Jenny came
into her room. "Brenda," she said.
"I think there is something for you
at the front door. Take your coat.
The wind is blowing very hard, and
you aren't dressed for the cold."

Brenda ran down and opened the door.
She found a piece of paper there.

FOLLOW THE BLUE PAPER FOOTSTEPS. YOUR DREAM IS DUE TO COME TRUE.

Brenda couldn't believe her eyes. There were big footprints cut out of bright blue paper all over. The footprints went across her porch, down the front steps, and along the sidewalk. They stopped at a house that was just two doors away.

"Why, this is Terry Fern's house," Brenda thought to herself. Terry sat next to her in class. Brenda followed the footsteps up the steps to the front door.

The door was open just a crack.
She followed the blue footprints
into the living room. It was very dark
inside the house. Brenda thought she
could hear someone laughing.

All at once the lights came on.
Brenda looked around the room. She
couldn't believe what she saw. It was
a party for her! All the boys and girls
from her new school were there. So were
her mother, father, and sister.

"You found all our clues," her friend
Terry said. "You should be chief private eye."
Brenda laughed. "I knew today was going
to be special," she said. And it was.

THINK ABOUT IT

1. Why was it a special day for Brenda?
2. Why wasn't Brenda happy?
3. What happened to make the day very special for Brenda?
4. Do you think that Brenda was lonely from then on?
5. Why didn't Jenny tell Brenda what was planned for her?
6. What is a friend? What can you do to be a good friend?

A GAME FOR FOUR PLAYERS

Have you ever thought about making up a game? The game that follows is a model. Follow the model, and have some fun.

Things You Will Need

1 big sheet of paper
50 white cards
1 marking pen
coloring pens
4 round game
  markers (4 colors)
a level place to work

Steps

1. Place the sheet of paper on a level
   work space.
2. Put one of the game markers
   at the lower left-hand part
   of the paper and draw around it.
3. Draw a weaving, turning road
   of marker circles across the sheet
   of paper.
4. When you have drawn your road, write
   START where it begins.
5. Draw an arrow around **START.**

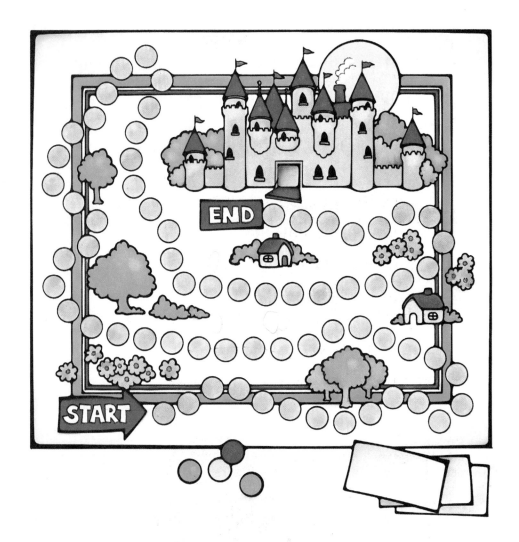

6. Draw a castle at the other end of the road. You may want to draw trees and a lawn around your castle. You may even want to color the trees and lawn green.

7. When you have drawn your castle, write the word **END** at the end of the road.

8. Write **CRAWL AHEAD ONE SPACE** on 10 of the cards.

9. Write **CRAWL AHEAD TWO SPACES** on 15 of the cards.

10. Write **HOP AHEAD FOUR SPACES** on 15 of the cards.

11. Write **STOP TO SING A SONG. MISS ONE TURN** on 5 of the cards.

12. Write **STOP TO FOLLOW A GIANT. GO BACK FOUR SPACES** on 5 of the cards.

If you have followed the model,
your game will look like the one
on the table below. Now read the
Rules of the Game. Follow the rules
and have some more fun!

RULES

Rules of the Game

1. Mix the cards, and stack them between the players.

2. Each player takes a marker and starts at the arrow.

3. The first player takes the top card from the stack and does what the card says. If the card says **STOP TO SING A SONG. MISS ONE TURN,** the player's marker doesn't move. It stays where it is until the other three have all had a turn.

4. Place the used cards in another stack. Use them when the first stack is gone.

5. Play until someone reaches the castle.

Let's All Go Singing

Soft snow is falling.
    Winter is here.
Get out your warm things.
    Cover your ears.
Put on your coats,
    And away we will go.
Let us all go singing,
    Out in the snow.

Lift up your voices,
    Sing loud and clear.
This is the very best
    Time of the year.
It's your fault
    If you miss all the fun.
Let us all go singing.
    Come, everyone!

WINTER GARDEN

There's a garden
   on my window pane.
It grows without
   seeds, sun, or rain.
What puts the
   lacy flowers there?
Frost and cold
   and wintry air.

Reading for Fun

Sometimes we read because we have
to know about something. What we have
to know may be for school or for work.
Or we may have to know how to get
someplace or how to do something.
We may even have to know what is
in a bottle, a can, or a box.

We can call this kind of reading
READING TO KNOW. There is another
kind of reading that can be called
READING FOR FUN.

When we read for fun, we do it because
we want to, not because we have to.
This kind of reading can take us to places
we have never been before. It can show us
people we have never met.

Do you want to know about people
who lived long ago? Read about them.
Do you want to know about other parts
of the world and the plants and animals
that live there? Read about them.
Do you want to know about a ball player,
a singer, or a private eye? You can read
about them, too.

The world of books is a very special
place. In it you will find kings and
queens, giants and genies, and boys
and girls like you. Open thc door and
walk in. You'll find that reading can be fun!

The Visit

"This looks like a very good place to visit," said Walter.

"I think so too," said Patty. "There is no limit to how good it could be. It's in a big field. We can play there. I would like to stay."

"It's OK," said Patty and Walter's father. "Just keep your jackets on and you won't look strange. Everyone will think you are like Mother and me."

"And try to be good," said Mother. "You were so bad last time!"

Patty and Walter were trying not to laugh. "We know," they said.

"Your room is on the third floor," the man said to Walter and Patty's father. "And children, your room is next door. The steps are right over there."

"Oh, that's OK," said Patty. "We'll just go in the window."

"What?" said the man.

"Patty!" said Mother. "You said you would be good!"

"Well, Mother," said Patty. "I am trying, but there is a limit to how good I can be!"

Patty and Walter were trying not to laugh as they ran up the steps.

"This looks like a very good room for our visit," said Walter. "Now we just have to find someplace to sleep."

"I could sleep on the floor," said Patty. "I am getting very good at it. But Mother will be upset if we don't sleep in the beds. So I am willing to try sleeping under one of them. After all, there is a limit to how bad I can be."

Patty picked up some paper and a pencil. She wrote the word food. "What would you like to eat?" she asked. "I will call down for some food."

"I want what I always have," said Walter.

"Me too," said Patty.

Patty sat down in the chair. "Hello, food people?" she said. "This is room 321. We need something to eat. We want green food on a silver dish. Then we want blue food on a gold dish. No. Not cold. Gold! Why are you so upset? OK. OK. Just send up two dishes of anything made with gum. Hello? Hello? No one is there. Oh, well. We have better things to do than eat."

Walter walked over to the window and looked across the field. "We should go out," he said. Then he looked down. "Patty," he shouted. "There is a chair down there. And in it is a sleeping stranger."

"You mean there is someone in a chair in that field?" asked Patty.

"No," said Walter. "He's got his chair on the porch. There is no one around."

Patty jumped up and looked down. She threw off her jacket. "Let's go!" she yelled. And out the window they went.

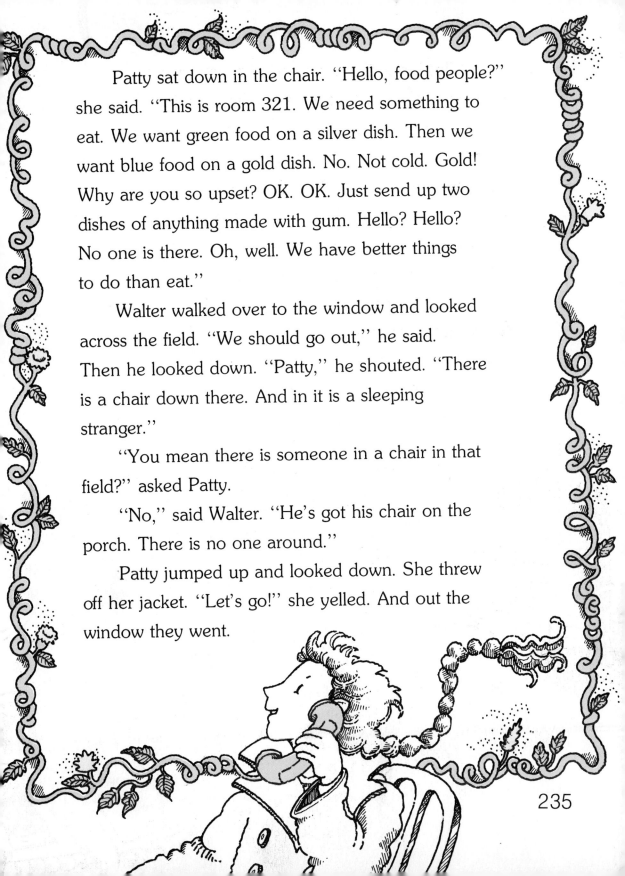

."Sing something, Patty," said Walter.

"OK," said Patty and she began in a soft voice.

"Sleeping stranger, can you hear us?
We have come to haunt you.
Sleeping stranger, can you see us?
We are here. We want you!"

The man opened one eye. "What?" he said.
"Haunt? Someone has come to haunt me? What would
cause someone to do that?"

Then the man saw Walter and Patty. He jumped
out of his chair. "Help," he yelled. "Flying children!
Watch out for flying children!"

The man ran through the room where the people were eating. Patty and Walter flew after him. They knew they should not. But they just couldn't help it. Then everyone stopped.

A woman with paper and a pencil came up to Walter and Patty. "I am from the TV," she said. "I want to tell everyone about you. What causes you to fly? Will you do it when you grow up?"

"I don't know what causes it," said Walter. "Our mother and father can't do it. But when I grow up, I will be flying. I am going to be a pilot. I'll work at the airport. And Patty is going to be a singer. She's got a good voice."

"I own this place," said a man. "You two can work here right now. Then my place can be on TV, too."

237

So now Patty and Walter and their mother and father
live at the big house. They do many things. They work
with the food people. All the food is blue or green.

Walter likes to fly the food to the tables. He's got
strong arms. Sometimes, he goes to the airport. He
is not a pilot yet. But he does use his arms to carry
children and small people back to the house when they
come for a visit.

238

Patty is a singer. One song that people like a lot is "Pilot, Where Is Your Field?" But there is one song they like best. This is how it goes.

"Flying is very good for your feet.
You can fly in the sky above the street.
But never fly when you are inside,
You will make a mess and have to hide."

THINK ABOUT IT

1. Why did Patty and Walter's father want them to keep their jackets on?

2. What does Patty want to be when she grows up? What does Walter want to be?

3. Why was the man in the field upset when he saw Patty and Walter?

4. Why would the woman from TV want to tell everyone about Patty and Walter?

5. Would you like to fly? Why or why not?

WRITE AND READ ABOUT IT

ONE ─────────────────────────────

Marching Along, 10-13

✎Think of words with sounds that you like. You might pick words like <u>slip</u>, <u>fish</u>, <u>flash</u>, or <u>twinkle</u>. Then make up a poem with the sound words. Here is a poem to look at.

fish flash

twinkle twinkle

slip slip slip!

📖*St. Patrick's Day in the Morning* by Eve Bunting (Houghton Mifflin Company). A boy and his dog have a march of their own.

The Marchers, 14-17

✎Does the color yellow make you feel bright and sunny? Then, how about blue, green, red, gold, gray, and brown? Pick the best words you know to write about how each color makes you feel.

📖 *Roger Was a Razor Fish and Other Poems* by Jill Bennett (Lothrop, Lee, & Shepard Books). This book is filled with cartoons and poems.

Pets for Bess, 18-23

✏️ The boy in the story uses his hands to see. You can use your hands to see, too. Feel some grass, some sand, and some rocks. Pick words to tell what you have seen with your hands. Then write about it.

📖 *The Beetle Bush* by Beverly Keller (Coward, McCann & Geoghegan, Inc.). Snails, beetles, and moles take over Arabelle's garden.

Why Are Some Days Cloudy?, 24-29

✏️ Think about clouds. Think about what it might be like to fly. What would you see? How would the air feel as you floated along? Be a cloud in your mind! Write about what you see and feel.

📖 *I Like Weather* by Aileen Fisher (Harper & Row Publishers, Inc.). Poems about sun, rain, clouds, and many other things.

241

The Singing Hen, 30-38

✎What gets you up? The sound of dishes? The cry of a baby? The rattle of a truck outside? Write about the first things you hear in a day. Do they make you hop out of bed? Or do they make you want to go back to sleep? Tell why.

📖*The Rooster Who Understood Japanese* by Yoshiko Uchida (Charles Scribner's Sons). Miyo finds a home for the rooster and makes a friend.

Timmy Turtle, 39-48

✎In the story, you found out what's not good for an old turtle. Now think about what's good and what is not good for some other things.

a glass dish	an old bike
a big fish	a funny hat

For each one, write as many things that are good and things that are not good as you can.

📖*Clams Can't Sing* by James Stevenson (Greenwillow Books). Beatrice and Benny show how good they are!

No Smiles Today, 49-55

✎ What are the things that you do well? Write them all down. They may be things you do at home, at school, or in other places. They may be big or small! Some of them could be funny, too. Here are some things to start you thinking.

I make Mom laugh.

I growl as well as most dogs.

Have fun bragging!

📖 *Jeremy Isn't Hungry* by Barbara Williams (E. P. Dutton). Taking care of a baby can be hard.

_____ TWO

The Boy From Zorgo, 58-65

✎ You have just landed on Zorgo! What will you find there? Will people have bright green hair and purple skin like Zerp? Will houses float or move around? How cold is it there? Write about Zorgo.

📖 *My Robot Buddy* by Alfred Slote (J. B. Lippincott Company). Jack gets a robot for his birthday.

243

Caught in a Storm, 66-67

✎In this poem some sounds are used over and over. You can play with the sounds of words, too. This sentence hisses with the sound of <u>s</u>:

Waves smash on sand, spill shells, and slip into the sea.

Write sentences about rockets that use words that have the **r** sound at the beginning, middle, or end.

📖 *The Great Blizzard* by Robert Bahr (Dandelion Press, Inc.). This is the story of a snowstorm in the 1880's.

Beavers, 68-74

✎Watch an animal. What does it like to do. Look at its face, feet, and tail. Write about what you see.

📖*Sea Otters* by Evelyn Shaw (Harper & Row Publishers). Susan learns about sea otters.

Play Ball! 75-83

✎What is it like where you play? How does it look? Is it a good place to play? How could it become a better place? Write about this place.

📖 *Somebody Stole Second* by Louise Munro Foley (Dell Publishing Co., Inc.). The base is missing, and the children must find it.

The Best Plan, 84-93

✎ Think about the things you like to do and when you like to do them. Then make a book about them. Use pictures and words to show how you would plan a day.

📖 *Jasper and the Hero Business* by Betty Horvath (Avon Books). Jasper longs to do something big.

_____ **THREE**

The Missing Clock, 96-104

✎ One day all the clocks in the world began to rattle. They bumped, shook, and flew into the air. Then, in a flash, they fell to the ground and broke!

Write an end to this story. Think about these things. How will people know when to do things? Will the words "on time" mean anything anymore?

📖 *Unhurry Harry* by Eve Merriam (Scholastic Book Services). Harry is not on time, but people keep pushing him.

Talking Hands, 105-110

✏️ Put your hand down on paper. Draw around it. Then, in the space outside the drawing, write about your hand. Tell what it looks like. Tell how it moves. Is your hand like any animal you know? Tell as much as you can about your hand.

📖 *Handmade ABC: A Manual Alphabet* by Linda Bourke (Addison-Wesley Publishing Co., Inc.). You can learn to spell with your fingers.

How the Finch Got Its Colors, 111-117

✏️ Write a story that tells how something came to be. Here are some thoughts to start you off.

1. Long ago, all snakes were fat.
2. The sun wasn't always in the sky. It started out on the land.

Think about what could make snakes slim or put the sun up in the sky. Then start a story.

📖*Hailstones and Halibut Bones* by Mary O'Neill (Doubleday & Co., Inc.). This fine book has poems about the colors of many things.

The Puzzle, 118-119

✎In "The Puzzle," the barnyard animals run away from the bee. In your mind, become the bee! Write to the rooster. Tell him all the good things about bees. Write about flying, flowers, or spring days. Buzz a little about yourself!

📖*Bees and Beelines* by Judy Hawes (Harper & Row Publishers, Inc.). A book of many good things to know about bees and what they do.

The Old House, 120-129

✎Think about what might happen if an old house could talk. What kinds of stories might it tell? Could they be funny stories about the people who lived there? Could they be happy stories?

Pretend you are that old house. Write a story about some of the people who have lived in you.

□ *Spooky Stuff* by Shari Lewis (Holt, Rinehart & Winston). This book will show you how to have fun with your friends.

FOUR _____

The Voice From the Deep, 132-141

✎ Think of things you could do with a box. Write down as many as you can. Here are some.

1. a place to hide
2. a carrying case
3. a drum
4. a place to keep air

Think hard! Funny uses for a box may just roll out of your mind!

□ *Busybody Nora* by Johanna Hurwitz (Dell Publishing Co., Inc.). Nora has fun getting city people to meet each other.

A Snail Takes a Walk/The Lesson, 142-143

✎ What other things that you know look something like silver ribbons? A string of clouds? Wet roads? How do they look alike? Think of some things that are as loud as a drum, as soft as a pillow, or as hot as the sun. Make a list.

Snail in the Woods by Joanne Ryder (Harper & Row Publishers). This book tells how one kind of snail lives and grows.

The Genie of the Lamp, 144-152

You just found an old bottle on the beach and brought it home. Boom! A mean, green genie pops out! What does it say? Then what happens? Write the end of this story to find out!

The Magician by Uri Shulevitz (The Macmillan Company). This is the story of magic at Passover.

How Does Your Garden Grow?, 153-160

Make up a new kind of plant. Make it a plant nobody has ever seen before! Where would it grow? How big or small would it be? Would it have flowers? Would it have odd parts? Name the new plant, draw its picture, and write about it.

Gardening Without Soil by Jan Johnsen (Harper & Row Publishers, Inc.). This book tells how many plants can grow in pots, bottles, and glasses.

Something for Tony, 161-169

✎ Think about a friend coming to stay with you for the summer. What would you plan to see and do? What kind of fun would you like your friend to have? Write a letter to him or her. Tell your friend about summer plans.

📖 *Window Wishing* by Jeanette Caines (Harper & Row Publishers, Inc.). Two children visit their grandmother.

FIVE _____

Work for Willy, 172-179

✎ If people all did the same work, many things would not get done. What work must be done to help people live well in your town? Write the names of as many kinds of work as you can find. Here are some.

build homes	grow food	make cars
build roads	sell food	write books

📖 *Giraffes* by Louise C. Brown (Dodd, Mead & Company). This book tells all about giraffes in Africa.

250

Suntime, 180-185

✎Pick something you want to write about. It could be something you like to do or a thought that pleases you. Next, make up some compound words you can use when you write. Here are some compound words about singing — roundsounds, silversongs, mouthmoves, keepsong.

Make up your own new words. Then write a story or poem using the best ones.

📖 *The Way to Start a Day* by Byrd Baylor (Charles Scribner's Sons). People from all over the world are happy as they get up with the sun.

Down Silver Streams, 186-187

✎Think of words that end with the same sound. Words like <u>hot</u>, <u>stop</u>, <u>play</u>, and <u>blue</u> have many words like them. Write them down.

Here are some that sound like the word follow.

    hello   pillow   show   shadow   yellow

Now use some of the words to make a funny sentence. Here is one.

    The shadow on the yellow pillow says hello!

📖 *The Moon's the North Wind's Cooky: Night Poems* edited by Susan Russo (Lothrop, Lee & Shepard Company). This small book is filled with special poems about nighttime.

Rumpelstiltskin, 189-197

✏️ If you could do anything you wanted, what would it be? Would you change the world in some way? Would you make something new? Would you become small enough to sit in a spoon? What would <u>you</u> do? Write about it. Tell why.

📖 *Kids Do Amazing Things* by Arthur Myers (Random House, Inc.). They may not spin straw into gold, but many children do great things!

City Fishing, 198-207

✏️ Begin writing a story about you and your friends. When you come to a turning point, flip a penny to find out what happens next. If the penny lands heads up, something good must happen. If it lands tails up, something must go wrong. Flip the penny two times before your story ends.

📖 *On the Way to the Movies* by Charlotte Herman (E. P. Dutton Company). Simon has to bring his little brother with him, and he's not happy.

——————————————————————— SIX

The Chief Private Eye, 210-220

✎ If you had to move away, would you miss anyone? What places and things would stay in your mind? Write about the people and places you would miss. Tell why you would think about them.

📖 *Something Queer on Vacation* by Elizabeth Levy (Delacorte Press). Jill and Gwen find out who's been messing up their sand castles.

A Game for Four Players, 221-226

✎ What do you like about games? What don't you like? Which do you like best? Why? Is it better to play without games? Write what you think.

📖 *Jumanji* by Chris Van Allsburg (Houghton Mifflin). Peter and Judy are playing a game about a jungle when they see a real lion.

253

Let's All Go Singing/Winter Garden, 227-228

✎Change the words of a song you know well. The song should be about winter. Here are some new words for the first part of "Row Row Row Your Boat."

Let's slide down the hill,

Can you come and play?

Now write new words for the end of the song. Sing it to see how they work. If you like, try writing new words for "Old MacDonald Had a Farm."

📖 *Moments: Poems About the Seasons,* edited by Lee Bennett Hopkins (Harcourt Brace Jovanovich Inc.). Fresh poems about the seasons will make your eyes and ears open to the little things around you.

Reading for Fun, 229-231

✎What is the best kind of story to read? Is it about real people and real things? Or is it about giants and genies riding the wind? Put some ideas for stories on little slips of paper. Roll up the slips, and put them in a box.

Put in some ideas for people, some for places, and some for things to happen. Put in more and more ideas as you think of them. When you have enough, pull out a few paper slips. Can you put the ideas on them into one story? Try!

Yet Another Big Fat Funny Silly Book by Stoo Hample (Delacorte Press). Silly riddles, jokes, pictures, and poems are fun to read.

The Visit, 232-239

How would you feel if you had wings? Would you cover them up and feel shy? Or would you be proud and puff out your chest? Make believe you can fly like the children in the story. What would you do? Write about the first day you flew.

Cloudy With a Chance of Meatballs by Judi Barrett (Atheneum Publishers). Food falls out of the sky over the town of Chewandswallow.

HELP WITH WORDS

airport

acorn   a seed from an oak tree
The squirrel likes that **acorn.**

airport   a place where jets take off and land
She went to the **airport** with her friend.

alarm   a bell
The **alarm** rang at six o'clock.

always   at all times
We have **always** lived in the city.

anger   a strong feeling of not liking something
The genie showed his **anger** by pounding the table.

animal   any living being, such as a girl or a pony
The lamb is a gentle **animal.**

another   one more
May I please have **another** glass of milk?

arrow   a mark that shows the way to go
Follow the **arrow** to the stamp show.

barn

bad   not good
Bad lighting may hurt your eyes.

barn   a place to keep farm animals
The animals stayed in the **barn** when it rained.

bean   a seed that can be used as food
Jack planted a **bean** in his garden.

bear   a very big animal with thick fur
The **bear** at the circus could ride a bike.

beauty   something that pleases
The picture showed the **beauty** of a rainbow.

begin   to start
The show will **begin** at noon.

borrow   to take something you plan to give back
You may **borrow** my book if you need it.

breeze   a light wind
A **breeze** blew the papers to the floor.

Cc

cabin a small house
We stayed in a **cabin** by the beach.

carry to take from one place to another
Eve will **carry** the box to the car.

catch to take hold of
You throw the ball, and I'll **catch** it.

cellar a room below the ground
I keep my old toys in the **cellar.**

clock

clock something we use for telling time
The **clock** has a small face.

Dd

dial the face of a watch or clock
The **dial** has a light so you can see
the time in the dark.

dull not bright
Gray is a **dull** color.

258

eagle   a kind of big bird
The **eagle** flew to that branch.

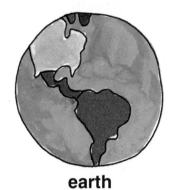

earth   the place on which we live
The **earth** moves around the sun.

earth

ever   at any time
Have you **ever** seen an eagle?

everywhere   all places
Mike goes **everywhere** on his bike.

finch   a small bird that sings
The **finch** is a pretty bird.

follow   to go next
I will go first, and Fay can **follow** me.

finch

food   the things we eat
You will be fat if you eat too much **food.**

freeze   to get very cold and hard
When water **freezes,** it becomes hard.

Gg

giraffe

garden   a place for flowers and plants

We have red roses in our **garden.**

giant   someone who is very big

The **giant** was as tall as a building.

giraffe   a kind of animal with a long neck

The **giraffe** likes to eat grass.

H h

happen   to take place

What will **happen** next?

hire   to give someone work

Mrs. Brown needs to **hire** someone to work in her shop.

huge   very big

The old tree looked **huge** next to the small boy.

I i

ice   water that is very cold and becomes hard

The **ice** will melt when it gets hot in the room.

jacket a kind of short coat

I wear my **jacket** when it's cold.

kitten a baby cat

The **kitten** likes milk.

knock to tap

Please **knock** before you come in.

leaf the part of a plant that grows from a stem

The **leaf** will turn red in the fall.

learn to find out

Did you **learn** how to make paper flowers?

lion

lion a kind of big cat

The trainer fed the **lion** at the circus.

listen to hear

No one will **listen** to me.

Mm

miller

many a lot of

Many children know how to ride a bike.

march to walk with an even step

We will **march** when the band plays.

middle the center

To play this game, someone must stand in the **middle** of the circle.

miller someone who works in a mill

The **miller** worked all day at the mill.

Nn

neck

neck the part of you just below your head

He's wearing a bib around his **neck.**

never at no time

My puppy will **never** growl if you give her a bone.

noise a loud sound

The **noise** hurt my ears.

oak a kind of tree
The birds made a nest in the **oak** tree.

once at one time
Once, I pitched for that team.

parrot a bird with bright colors
My **parrot** is bright green.

picture

patch a covering for a torn or worn place
I can **patch** my old sweater.

picture a drawing or painting
I painted a **picture** of my house.

pitcher someone who throws a ball to a batter
Our **pitcher** can throw a fast ball.

queen a woman who is head of her land
The **queen** lived in a castle.

quick fast
She is a **quick** runner.

rainy   having much rain

On **rainy** days, we play inside.

robin   a kind of bird with a red breast

The **robin** has a nest in the tree.

root   the part of a plant that is under the ground

The tree gets water from the ground through its **roots.**

robin

save   to keep

Save those bones for our dog.

shine   to give light

The sun makes the windows **shine.**

spin   to turn around and around

She can **spin** the ball with one hand.

squirrel   a small animal with a big tail

The **squirrel** likes seeds.

squirrel

store   a shop

We can get some food in that **store.**

tiny small

The baby took the toy in his **tiny** hand.

tomorrow the day after today

I cannot go today, but I will go **tomorrow.**

town small city

We have many shops in our **town.**

turtle a small animal with a shell on its back

The **turtle** will hide in its shell if you make a loud sound.

turtle

ugly not nice

That old house looks **ugly.**

upset to make someone feel bad

We **upset** Mom and Dad when we are late for lunch.

urge to try to get someone to do something

The shouts from the crowd **urge** the team to win.

visit   to go to see someone or some place
Grandpa likes to **visit** us.

voice   a sound coming from the mouth
He has a good singing **voice.**

wad   a small lump
I stepped on a **wad** of gum.

wallet

wallet   a small flat case for carrying bills
My **wallet** has nothing in it.

watch   to look at
I like to **watch** TV.

weep   to cry
The sad show made me **weep.**

wind   air that moves
The **wind** howled through the trees.

Yy

yarn   something used in work such as weaving

What can I make with this red **yarn?**

year   365 or 366 days

How many **years** have you lived on this street?

young   having an early age

My little sister is too **young** to go to school.

you're   a short form for *you are*

You're sitting in my seat.

you've   a short form for *you have*

You've pitched a good game.

yo-yo

yo-yo   a toy that winds on a string

I can make the **yo-yo** go up and down.

Zz

zebra   a black-and-white animal

The **zebra** likes to run in the field.

New Words

The following words are introduced in *Marching Along.* Each is listed beside the number of the page on which it appears for the first time. The words printed in black are developmental words, and those printed in blue are new words that pupils can decode independently.

With the exception of derivatives (*catcher,* for example), only base forms are given. Note, however, that the skill of forming the plural of a noun by adding -*es* is developed in selection 18. Forming the plural possessive is developed in selection 26. Dropping the final *e* before adding -*ed* to a verb form is developed in selection 3. Adding -*es* to a verb form is developed in selection 18. Adding -*er* to an adjective or adverb without a base change is developed in selection 13. Adding -*est* to an adjective or adverb is developed in selection 24.

Selection 2
15. march
   marcher
16. crowd
   feet
   should
   would
17. alone
   began
   could

Selection 3
18. Bess
   laugh
   rich
   such
19. shell
20. clean
   gleam
   sand
   team

21. much
22. case

Selection 4
24. cloudy
   fair
   goes
   snowy
25. drop
   hair
   water
26. air
   become
   begin
   gas
   rainy
27. ice
28. below

Selection 5
30. any
   flew
   milk
   sell
   spin
31. thought
   threw
   town
32. brought
   cutter
   spinner
   yarn
33. late
34. ought
35. bragger
36. blew
   more
38. teach

Selection 6
39. anything
   bank
   other
   Timmy Turtle
   turtle
   world
40. roll
41. an
   heard
   nothing
   someday
   there's
42. hate
   hear
   listen
44. son
45. held

Selection 7
49. baby
both
sister
50. mouth
put
she's (is)
teeth
they're
you're
51. bar
buggy
push
steady
52. head
paper
read (e)
we're

Selection 8
58. bus
Butch
jacket
moon
store
Zorgo
59. rocket
space
spaceship
wallet
60. purple
truck

61. before
Earth
62. lady
pull
sold
63. Zerp
bought
ship
64. sometime

Selection 9
66. above
ahead
almost
caught
storm
67. done
watch

Selection 10
68. beaver
69. also
build
flat
front
learn
many
most
swim
tail

70. dam
doe
rat
shallow
twig
71. branch
72. always
its

Selection 11
75. Grant
match
score
Terry
76. batter
bench
catch
hitch
mad
pitch
pitcher
player
runner
77. base
mask
mitt
patch
sweater
weren't
78. Mrs. Singer
task

79. gave
pocket
80. switch

Selection 12
84. Bob
Bud
Ford
85. form
lump
oil
spoil
stamp
86. another
boil
I'll
mean
87. bump
ever
short
88. we'll
89. jump
90. bunch
read (ē)
write
91. never
wrote
92. he's (is)
93. he'll

269

Selection 19

142. across
been
early
instead
porch
ribbon
shine
silver
weave

143. freeze
lesson
lonely
once
roadway
since
through
trucker
wagon

Selection 20

144. genie
gentle
morning
table

145. huge
weigh

146. anger
dirty
feelings
hunger
ready

147. age

148. brave
gem
real
urge
wrinkle

149. beside

150. even
giant
without

Selection 21

153. acorn
garden
grow
oak
petal
sunflower

154. ground
picture
squirrel

155. bean
half
tough

156. sunshine

157. enough
force
root
rough

158. leaf
own

Selection 22

161. great
letter
news
winner

162. country
dear
fresh
Ray
summer

163. special

164. puff
smoke
sniff

165. young

166. himself

167. barn
touch

168. pony
who's (is)

Selection 23

172. animal
giraffe
sigh
Willy

173. high
neck
stream
stretch
tire
zebra

174. travel

175. fire

178. hire

179. besides

Selection 24

180. guest
guide
suntime
wristwatch

181. change
gone
middle
overhead
shadow
size

182. cannot
haze
hour
range
strange

183. dial
sundial

184. metal
round

Selection 25

186. dream
everywhere

187. breeze
cough
tear (ar)
tiny
wear

188. bad
bear
lion